BASIC theory of struc

Butterworths BASIC Series includes the following titles:

BASIC stress analysis
BASIC thermodynamics and heat transfer
BASIC materials studies
BASIC mechanical vibrations
BASIC numerical mathematics
BASIC matrix methods
BASIC statistics
BASIC hydrology
BASIC hydraulics
BASIC aerodynamics
BASIC soil mechanics
BASIC molecular spectroscopy
BASIC interactive graphics
BASIC economics
BASIC investment analysis

BASIC theory of structures

K R F Andrews
Department of Civil Engineering, King's College, London

Butterworths
London . Boston . Durban . Singapore . Sydney . Toronto . Wellington

First published 1985

© Butterworth & Co. (Publishers) Ltd 1985

British Library Cataloguing in Publication Data
    Andrews, K. R. F.
    BASIC theory of structures.—(Butterworths
    BASIC series)
    1. Civil engineering—Data processing   2. Basic
    (Computer program language)
    I. Title
    624′.028′5424   TA345

    ISBN 0–408–01357–5

Library of Congress Cataloging in Publication Data

Andrews, K. R. F.
    BASIC theory of structures.

    (Butterworths BASIC series)
    Bibliography: p.
    Includes index.
    1. Structures, Theory of—Computer programs.
2. Basic (Computer program language)   I. Title
II. Series
TA647.A55 1985   624.1′7′0285424   85–4238
ISBN 0–408–01357–5

Filmset by Mid-County Press, London SW15
Printed and bound in Scotland by
Thomson Litho Ltd, East Kilbride

Preface

An understanding of the methods of analysis and an ability to use them effectively and accurately are essential elements of the creative process of design in many branches of engineering. With the aid of computers, engineers have repeatable accuracy at all times and can analyse structures of considerable complexity in a very short time. However, understanding of the methods of analysis must be painstakingly learned while lessons of effective use are gained over years of practical application. It may be argued that computers have rendered those two processes obsolete but effective and economic use of computer based analysis and design can only come from an understanding of the principles used in the programs and their limitations.

This book attempts to increase understanding of elementary structural analysis and the powerful assistance computers can provide. At the early stage of development, for which this book is intended, it is hoped that the theoretical background and computer programming will mutually assist one another. The programs provided follow the analytical methods very closely and therefore are lacking in the sophistication of more advanced and more efficient analytical programs. In this way, the student should be able to follow through the programs and print out information or make simple changes as required. Indeed, the problems given at the end of each chapter encourage this as well as the use of hand calculations in the early stages.

The book covers topics commonly found in first year undergraduate courses in Structures such as statically determinate trusses and beams. In addition, methods involving virtual work are presented.

After a chapter on the elements of the BASIC language and an introduction to the fundamentals of structural analysis, Chapter 3 presents the basic numerical methods, solution of simultaneous equations and numerical integration, employed in the programs in following chapters.

Chapter 4 deals with the force analysis of statically determinate pin-jointed trusses using resolution at joints and tension coefficients. Chapter 5 continues with the analysis of pin-jointed trusses using the Williot-Mohr diagrams and virtual work methods for joint displacements.

Following a brief discussion of bending moment and shear force, Chapter 6 presents three methods of determining beam deflection; Macaulay's double integration method, Area–Moment theorems and virtual work. The importance of influence line diagrams in design is recognised in Chapter 7 in which influence line diagrams for simply supported and hinged beams and truss member forces are investigated.

The programs listed in each chapter are written in the most standard form of BASIC possible. In fact, they were developed on an Apple II computer using Applesoft. However, there should be little trouble in running them on any computer with the BASIC language facility. Although each program has been tested, no guarantee of freedom from bugs or malfunction due to incorrectly presented or unusual forms of data, can be given. The author is continually applying and testing these programs and will be pleased to try and help anyone encountering problems.

I am grateful to Anne Alexander, Jan Andrews and the Civil Engineering Department of King's College London for help in preparing the manuscript.

KRFA
1985

Contents

Chapter 1

Introduction to BASIC

1.1 The BASIC approach

The programs presented in this book are written in the BASIC programming language which is now widely available on microcomputers. Such programs require no actual compilation and are thus easy to run and edit. However, the language lacks the structure of FORTRAN. In particular, variables cannot be isolated within a subroutine enabling the subroutine to be transferred easily from one program to another. Nevertheless, an attempt has been made to standardize subroutines so that they are almost identical wherever they appear. Thus the subroutine for solving sets of simultaneous equations will use the same variables, arrays and line numbers in all applications.

As in other volumes in this series, the book does not set out formally to teach you the BASIC language but endeavours to increase your knowledge of the language by studying its application to structural problems and using the programs to solve the problems. A short description of the grammar and syntax of simple BASIC is given in the following sections.

1.2 The elements of BASIC

1.2.1 Expressions

Most engineering problems can be reduced to the evaluation of expressions or formulae which are written, in their most general form, in terms of numerical constants, variables and functions (i.e. sin, cos) together with operators. The computer will evaluate these expressions very rapidly, very accurately and as many times as you wish. The result of the evaluation of an expression can be 'stored' in a variable and used in a subsequent expression. If several of these expressions are written in order of their evaluation then a simple 'program' has been written. There are 'rules' which must be followed in writing expressions. All constants or numbers are designated real

1

(e.g. 36.1) or integer (e.g. 36). An exponential form is used to represent large or small numbers (e.g. 3.61E6 represents 3.61×10^6). Variables (which can be considered as pigeon-hole stores) are represented by a letter, a letter followed by a letter or a letter followed by a number (e.g. E, EE or E1). It should be noted that in standard BASIC variables with more than two characters are distinguished only by the first two characters, a frequent source of error for beginners.

The BASIC language has several built-in functions. SQR(X) gives the square root of the argument X which can be a number (non-negative in this case), a variable or an expression. For trigonometrical functions (SIN(X), COS(X), etc.), X is in radians. Other functions include a natural logarithm and the exponential (LOG(X) and EXP(X)), ABS which gives the absolute value of the argument and INT which gives the integer part of the argument.

The operators (plus, minus, etc.) have a hierarchy of evaluation which in descending order is:

to the power of ($\wedge$)
multiply ($*$) and divide (/)
add ($+$) and subtract ($-$)

with evaluation of equal hierarchy from left to right in an expression. Parts of the expression within brackets are evaluated separately. Hence the expression $\dfrac{a+b}{3c}$ may be written (A + B)/(3*C) with (A + B) and (3*C) being calculated before division. Note that A + B/3*C has a different value!

1.2.2 Program structure and assignment statements

A BASIC program is a sequence of statements which define a procedure for the computer to follow. As it follows this procedure, the computer allocates values to each of the variables. The values of some of these variables may be specified by data that are input to the program. Others are generated in the program using, for instance, the assignment statement. This has the form

line number [LET] variable = mathematical expression

where the word LET is usually optional and therefore omitted. As an example, the root of a quadratic equation

$$x_1 = \frac{-b + \sqrt{b^2 - 4ac}}{2a}$$

may be obtained from a statement such as

$$100 \ X1 = (-B + SQR(B\hat{\ }2 - 4_*A_*C))/(2_*A)$$

It is important to realise that an assignment statement is not itself an equation. Rather, it is an instruction to the computer to give the variable on the left-hand side the numeric value of the expression on the right-hand side. It is therefore possible to have a statement

$$50 \ X = X + 1$$

which increases by 1 the value of X. Each variable can have only one value at any time unless it is subscripted (see Section 1.2.7).

Note that all BASIC statements (i.e. all the program lines) are numbered. The line number defines the order in which such statements are executed.

1.2.3 Input

For interactive or 'conversational' programs the user specifies variables by inputting data in response to prompts from the computer as the program is running. The statement has the form

line number INPUT variable 1 [, variable 2,...]

e.g.

20 INPUT A, B, C

When the program is run the computer prints ? as it reaches this statement and waits for the user to type values for the variables, e.g.

? 5, 10, 15

which makes A = 5, B = 10 and C = 15 in the example above.

An alternative form of data input is useful if there are many data or if the data are not to be changed by the user (e.g. a range of Young's Modulus values). For this type of data specification there is a statement of the form

line number READ variable 1[, variable 2,...]

e.g.

20 READ A, B, C

with an associated statement (or number of statements) of the form

line number DATA number 1 [, number 2,...]

e.g.

1 DATA 5, 10, 15

or

    1 DATA 5
    2 DATA 10
    3 DATA 15

DATA statements can be placed anywhere in a program – it is often convenient to place them at the beginning of the program so that they can be easily changed.

When using built-in data it is sometimes necessary to read data from their start more than once during a single program run. This is done using the statement

    line number RESTORE

(though it has not been used in this book).

An INPUT statement may contain text, enclosed in quotes, which will appear on the screen. Thus

    20 INPUT "A ="; A

will print

    A =

and await the value you type in. Note "?" does not appear in this case.

1.2.4 Output

Output of data and the results of calculations, etc. is implemented by using a statement of the form

    Line number PRINT list

where the list may contain variables or expressions, e.g.

    200 PRINT A, B, C, A$\ast$B/C

text enclosed in quotes, e.g.

    10 PRINT "INPUT A, B, C IN MM"

or mixed text and variables, e.g.

    300 PRINT "PRESSURES ARE"; P; "N/MM^2"

The items in the list are separated by commas or semi-colons. Commas give tabulations in columns, each about 15 spaces wide, while a semi-colon suppresses this spacing. If a semi-colon is placed at the end of a list it has the function of suppressing the line feed. If the list is left empty a blank line is printed.

The necessity of using PRINT statements in association with both 'run-time' input (to indicate what input is required) and READ/DATA statements (because otherwise the program user has no record of the data) should be noted.

1.2.5 Conditional statements

It is often necessary to enable a program to take some action if, and only if, some condition is fulfilled. This is done with a statement of the form

> line number IF expression 1 conditional operator expression 2 THEN line number or expression

where the possible conditional operators are

> $=$ equals
> $\langle \rangle$ not equal to
> $<$ less than
> $< =$ less than or equal to
> $>$ greater than
> $> =$ greater than or equal to

For example, a program could contain the following statements if it is to stop when a zero value of A is input

> 20 INPUT A
> 30 IF A $< >$ 0 THEN 50
> 40 STOP
> 50 ...

In this example, note the statement

> line number STOP

which stops the run of a program. The statement

> line number END

may be used at the end of a program though this is not essential.

1.2.6 Loops

There are several means by which a program can repeat some of its procedure. The simplest such statement is

> line number GO TO line number

This statement could be used with the conditional statement example above so that the program continues to request values of A until the user inputs zero.

The most common way of performing loops is with a starting statement of the form

line number FOR variable = expression 1 TO expression 2 [STEP expression 3]

where the step is assumed to be unity if [STEP expression] is omitted. The finish of the loop is signified by a statement

line number NEXT variable

where the same variable is used in both FOR and NEXT statements. Its value should not be changed in the intervening lines.

A loop is used if, for example, N sets of data have to be READ and their reciprocals printed, e.g.

```
10 READ N
20 PRINT "NUMBER", "RECIPROCAL"
30 FOR I = 1 TO N
40 READ A
50 PRINT A, 1/A
60 NEXT I
```

Loops can also be used to generate data. Consider the example given below of a simple temperature conversion program:

```
10 PRINT "CENTIGRADE", 'FAHRENHEIT"
20 FOR C = 0 TO 100 STEP 5
30 PRINT C, 9*C/5 + 32
40 NEXT C
```

1.2.7 Subscripted variables

It is sometimes very convenient to allow a single variable to have a number of different values during a single program run. For instance, if a program contains data for several different forces in a member, it is convenient for these to be called $Q(1)$, $Q(2)$, $Q(3)$, etc. instead of $Q1$, $Q2$, $Q3$, etc. It is then possible for a single statement to perform calculations for all the forces, e.g.

```
50 FOR I = 1 TO N
60 V(I) = Q(I)/A
70 NEXT I
```

which determines the stress in the member (which is of cross-sectional area A) for each force.

A non-subscripted variable has a single value associated with it and if a subscripted variable is used it is necessary to provide space for all the values. This is done with a dimensioning statement of the form

line number DIM variable 1 (integer 1) [, variable 2 (integer 2), ...]

e.g.

20 DIM V(20), Q(20), A(10,20)

which allows up to 21 values of V and Q since Q(0) and V(0) are allowed. V and Q are one-dimensional arrays or vectors, A is a two-dimensional array or matrix of particular use in structural analysis. The DIM statement must occur before the subscripted variables are first used.

On some computers it is possible to use a dimension statement of a different form, e.g.

20 DIM V(N), Q(N)

where the value of N has been previously defined. This form, when available, has the advantage of not wasting storage space.

1.2.8 Subroutines

Sometimes a sequence of statements needs to be accessed more than once in the same program. Instead of merely repeating these statements it is better to put them in a subroutine. The program then contains statements of the form

line number GOSUB line number

When the program reaches this statement it branches (i.e. transfers control) to the second line number. The sequence of statements starting with this second line number ends with a statement

line number RETURN

and the program returns control to the statement immediately after the GOSUB call.

Subroutines can be placed anywhere in the program but it is usually convenient to position them at the end, separate from the main program statements.

Another reason for using a subroutine occurs when a procedure is written which is required in more than one program. In subroutines it is sometimes desirable to use less common variable names (e.g. X9 instead of X) so that the possibility of the same variable name being used with a different meaning in separate parts of the program is minimised.

1.2.9 Other statements

(1) Explanatory remarks or headings which are not to be output can be inserted into a program using

line number REM comment

Any statement beginning with the word REM is ignored by the computer. On some computers it is possible to include remarks on the same line as other statements.

(2) Non-numeric data (e.g. words) can be handled by string variables. A string is a series of characters within quotes (e.g. "PRESSURE") and a string variable is a letter followed by a $ sign (e.g. A$). String variables are particularly valuable when printed headings need to be changed.

(3) Multiple branching can be done with statements of the form

line number ON expression THEN line number 1 [, line number 2, ...]

and

line number ON expression GOSUB line number 1 [, line number 2, ...]

When a program reaches one of these statements it branches to line number 1 if the integer value of the expression is 1, to line number 2 if the expression is 2 and so on. An error message is printed if the expression gives a value less than 1 or greater than the referenced line numbers.

(4) Functions other than those built into the language such as $SIN(X)$, etc. can be created by using a DEF statement. For example

10 DEF FNA(X) = $X^3 + X^2$

defines a cubic function which can be recalled later in the program as FNA (variable) where the value of this variable is substituted for X. A defined function is of use where an algebraic expression is to be evaluated several times in a program. (These last two statement forms have not been used in this book).

(5) Several statements can be written on a line. They are separated by colons. Thus

40 FOR I = 1 TO N: A(I) = B^N:NEXT I

gives a complete loop with only one line number. This is done usually to economise on the length of listings and, if overdone, makes the reading of the program very difficult. With consideration of readability, this has been used widely in the program listings in this book. It should be noted that any statements following a conditional statement on such a line will be ignored!

1.3 Checking programs

Most computers give a clear indication if there are grammatical (syntax) errors in a BASIC program. Program statements can be modified by retyping them completely or by using special editing procedures. The majority of syntax errors are easy to locate but if a variable has been used with two (or more) different meanings in separate parts of the program some 'mystifying' errors can result.

It is not sufficient for the program to be just grammatically correct – it must also give the correct answers. A program should therefore be checked either by using data which give a known solution or by hand calculation.

If the program is to be used with a wide range of data or by users other than the program writer, it is necessary to check that all parts of it function. It is also important to ensure that the program does not give incorrect yet plausible answers when 'nonsense' data are input. It is quite difficult to make programs completely 'userproof' and they become somewhat lengthy by so doing. The programs in this book have been kept as short as possible for the purpose of clarity and may not therefore be fully 'userproof'.

1.4 Different computers and variants of BASIC. Data storage and printing

The examples in this book use a simple version of BASIC that should run on most computers, even those with small storage capacity. In some versions of BASIC, multiple assignments are possible such as

$$1000 \ A(0) = B(0) = C(0) = D(0) = 0$$

which avoids four separate lines or four separate statements on one line. These have been avoided in this book.

There is one important feature which distinguishes computers, particularly microcomputers with visual display units (VDU). This concerns the number of columns available across each line and the number of lines that are visible on the screen. Simple modifications to some of the example programs may be necessary to fit the output to a particular microcomputer. TAB printing is a useful facility for this purpose.

Various enhancements of BASIC have been made since its

inception – these have been implemented on a number of computer systems. The programs in this book could be rewritten to take account of some of these 'advanced' features. For example, the ability to use long variable names (e.g. VELOCITY instead of say V or V1) makes it easier to write unambiguous programs. Other advanced facilities include more powerful looping and conditional statements and independent subroutines which make structured programs easier to write. Expressed simply, structured programming involves the compartmentalisation of programs and minimises branching resulting from statements containing 'GOTO line number' and 'THEN line number'. Good program structure is advantageous in long programs.

Output only to the VDU has been used in all programs. Assignment of output to a line printer would obviously give a more useful hard copy of the results. The instructions for this are dependent on the type of computer being used and for this reason it has been avoided in the text. The same is true of the storage of data on tapes or discs; a very important facility when several different solutions of a large problem are required. Nevertheless, the problems at the end of each chapter encourage the user to produce his own versions of the programs with these facilities included.

1.5 Summary of BASIC statements

Assignment

LET	Computes and assigns value
DIM	Allows space for subscripted variables

Input

INPUT	Reads data from 'run-time' keyboard input
READ	Reads data from DATA statements
DATA	Storage area for data
RESTORE	Restores data to its start

Output

PRINT	Prints output list

Program control

STOP	Stops program
IF...THEN	Conditional branching
GO TO	Unconditional branching
FOR...TO...STEP	Opens loop
NEXT	Closes loop
GOSUB	Transfers control to subroutine

RETURN	Return from subroutine
ON...THEN	Multiple branching
ON...GOSUB	Multiple subroutine transfer
END	Last line of program

Comment
REM	Comment in program

Functions
SQR	Square root
SIN	Sine (angle in radians)
COS	Cosine (angle in radians)
ATN	Arctangent (gives angle in radians)
LOG	Natural logarithm (base e)
EXP	Exponential
ABS	Absolute value
INT	Integer value
DEF FN	Defined function

1.6 Bibliography

The books noted below represent only a fraction of those available on
BASIC programming.

[1] Alcock, D., *Illustrating BASIC*, Cambridge University Press, (1977).
[2] Forsyth, R., *The BASIC Idea*, Chapman and Hall, (1978).
[3] Gottfried, B. S., *Programming with BASIC – Schaum's Outline Series*, McGraw-Hill, (1975).
[4] Kemeny, J. G. and Kurtz, T. E., *Basic Programming*, Wiley, (1968).
[5] Monro, D. M., *Interactive Computing with BASIC*, Arnold, (1974).

Chapter 2

Introduction to structural analysis

2.1 The aims of structural analysis

The analysis of a structure involves the determination of the forces and stresses at some or all points or in the individual members forming the structures. In addition, strains and deflections are calculated. These are required in one of two areas,

(1) Design: from a sketch or drawing of a proposed structure, the basic dimensions are determined and an analysis is carried out. The results of this analysis will indicate whether excessive forces, stresses, strains or displacements are developed. Dimensions or materials may then be altered, if necessary, and re-analysis takes place. Thus design requires a recurrent application of analysis.

(2) Checking of existing structures: a bridge or building may be required to support additional loading. An analysis with the increased loading will indicate the ability of the existing structure to support the load or those regions that require strengthening or alteration.

This book will introduce you to the analysis of simple structures and show you many of the simplifications and assumptions made in analysing structures.

2.2 Idealisation of structures

You will see that many of the drawings and figures of structures shown in the book are simply line drawings without form, shape or detailed foundations. This is the usual simplification process when first analysing a proposed structure. It is part of the art and skill of the engineer to transform these simplified calculations into the final assembled product. Some of this would form a textbook on design but much of it is developed with experience.

2.3 The principles of structural analysis

Structural analysis is a specialized area of stress analysis and the theory is based on the same three principles.

(1) Equilibrium of forces: the forces acting on a stationary structure must be in static equilibrium (dynamic equilibrium in the case of a moving body). This applies to the whole structure as well as parts or sections of it and there is frequent reference to external or internal forces which are self-explanatory.

(2) Compatibility of strains and displacements: this is the condition that the structure must fit together before and after loading. It must hold for all parts and sections of the structure.

(3) Constitutive relation: the stresses and strains developed within the structure must be consistent with the stress/strain law of the material used.

These conditions are required for any valid analysis of a structure, however complex the method used. In this book we consider structures for which each condition may be applied separately or sequentially for the determination of the required quantities. Most structures require the simultaneous consideration of these principles to effect an analysis.

In addition to these conditions, two basic assumptions are frequently made in elementary structural analysis. The first is the assumption of *small displacements* (or small strains). This ensures that any displacement of the structure during loading is small enough not to affect the position and orientation of the loading. If this is so, only a single force analysis is required. If it is not so, then non-linear analysis must be used. This does not mean that displacements are negligible and the interpretation of the meaning of 'small' will vary with structural type and material.

The second assumption is encompassed in the *Principle of Superposition*. If a structure supports several loads acting together, then the principle states that the displacement, force, stress, etc. at a point within the structure is the sum of these quantities due to each load acting alone. This is only valid when the material from which the structure is composed remains within its linear range when all loads are acting together.

2.4 Units

The SI units of force and length are the Newton (N) and the metre (m). The millimetre (mm) is frequently used as a length unit in structural analysis since this avoids the use of decimal points on drawings. Further, the unit of stress N/mm^2 produces far more convenient numbers.

2.5 The scope of the book

Where possible, a logical sequence of chapters has been employed. However, in moving from one structural type to another a new start is frequently required. For the most part, the chapters form self-contained groups with cross-referencing where useful.

Statistically determinate pin-jointed trusses and beams form the broad range of structures considered.

2.6 References

The list below includes those referred to in the text and others providing suitable background material.

[1] Krylov, V. I., *Approximate Calculations of Integrals*, trans. A. H. Stroud, Macmillan, New York, (1962).
[2] Iremonger, M. J., *BASIC Stress Analysis*, Butterworth Scientific, (1982).
[3] Jenkins, W. M. *Structural Mechanics and Analysis*, Level IV/V, Van Nostrand Reinhold, (1982).
[4] Coates, R. C., Coutie, M. G., Kong, F. K. *Structural Analysis*, Nelson, (1980).
[5] Mason, J. C., *BASIC Numerical Mathematics*, Butterworths, (1983).
[6] Francis, A. J., *Introducing Structures*, Pergamon Press, (1980).

Chapter 3

Numerical analysis

ESSENTIAL THEORY

3.1 Introduction

Communications between structural engineers about structural behaviour usually involve numbers rather than theories or differential equations. A 'feel' for the structure's response to loading is obtained from a knowledge of maximum deflections and stresses or forces. Thus the objective of structural analysis is to produce numbers representing various quantities. The structural engineer is not satisfied with just producing an algebraic formula or differential equation to define the structural response; he wishes to use these to find the actual numerical values. Therefore the branch of mathematics known as 'numerical analysis' is of considerable importance to the engineer.

Of course, computers are now used to produce our numbers and a calculation method is converted into algorithmic form, rather like a formula for the purposes of writing a program. However, the calculation methods are designed to give numbers rather than just describe the problem.

Two areas of numerical analysis are dealt with in this chapter. The solution of simultaneous equations is an important process in structural analysis, particularly when dealing with the complexities of real structures. Numerical integration enables the value of a definite integral of a function to be determined without reference to well known (or obscure) analytical solutions.

3.2 The solution of simultaneous equations

We are concerned with determining $\mathbf{x}$ in the equation

$$\mathbf{A}\mathbf{x} = \mathbf{b} \tag{3.1}$$

The vector $\mathbf{x}$ is a column vector of the unknown quantities, $x_1, x_2, \ldots x_n$, $\mathbf{A}$ is the square $(n \times n)$ matrix of the coefficients of x_1, x_2, etc. in each equation and $\mathbf{b}$ is a column vector. Thus the equations,

$$a_{11}x_1 + a_{12}x_2 + a_{13}x_3 = b_1$$
$$a_{21}x_2 + a_{22}x_2 + a_{23}x_3 = b_2$$
$$a_{31}x_2 + a_{32}x_2 + a_{33}x_3 = b_3$$

are written,

$$\begin{bmatrix} a_{11} & a_{12} & a_{13} \\ a_{21} & a_{22} & a_{23} \\ a_{31} & a_{32} & a_{33} \end{bmatrix} \begin{bmatrix} x_1 \\ x_2 \\ x_3 \end{bmatrix} = \begin{bmatrix} b_1 \\ b_2 \\ b_3 \end{bmatrix}$$

for three equations.

It should be noted that for successful solution there must be n independent equations in the n unknowns $\mathbf{x}$. This means that none of the equations must be combinations of the others which implies that $|\mathbf{A}| \neq 0$. If $|\mathbf{A}| = 0$ the the matrix $\mathbf{A}$ is said to be SINGULAR and no solution of the equations is possible.

The most common computer based method of solving the above equations is that of Gaussian Elimination and Back Substitution. In fact the method is identical to that used in hand calculations. Firstly x_1 is eliminated from all equations succeeding the first; this will change the coefficients of the succeeding equations and set $a_{21}, a_{31} \ldots$ to zero. Then x_2 is eliminated from all equations succeeding the second equation which further modifies the coefficients and sets a'_{32}, $a'_{42} \ldots$ to zero. This elimination process continues until only one non-zero coefficient in the last equation remains enabling x_n (x_3 in our equations) to be calculated. x_{n-1} can then be found from the last but one elimination equation and so on by back substitution until all values of $\mathbf{x}$ have been found.

As an example, consider the process applied to the solution of the following equations,

$$4x_1 + 3x_2 + 2x_3 = 1 \qquad (1)$$
$$2x_1 + 6x_2 + 2x_3 = 2 \qquad (2)$$
$$1x_1 + 3x_2 + 7x_3 = 3 \qquad (3)$$

(a) Eliminate x_1 from equations (2) and (3)

$$4x_1 + 3x_2 + 2x_3 = 1 \qquad (1)$$
$$4.5x_2 + x_3 = 1.5 \qquad (2) - \tfrac{1}{2}(1) = (2a)$$
$$2.25x_2 + 6.5x_3 = 2.75 \qquad (3) - \tfrac{1}{4}(1) = (3a)$$

(b) Eliminate x_2 from equation (3a)

$$4x_1 + 3x_2 + 2x_3 = 1 \qquad (3a)$$
$$4.5x_2 + x_3 = 1.5 \qquad (2a)$$
$$6x_3 = 2 \qquad (3a) - \tfrac{1}{2}(2a) = (3b)$$

End of Elimination

(c) From (3b) $x_3 = 0.333$

(d) From (2a) $4.5x_2 + 0.333 = 1.5$

$$x_2 = \frac{1.5 - 0.333}{4.5} = 0.259$$

(e) From (1) $4x_1 + 3(0.259) + 2(0.333) = 1$

$$x_1 = \frac{1 - 3(0.259) - 2(0.333)}{4} = -0.111$$

End of Back Substitution

The solution is

$$\begin{bmatrix} x_1 \\ x_2 \\ x_3 \end{bmatrix} = \begin{bmatrix} -0.111 \\ 0.259 \\ 0.333 \end{bmatrix}$$

We can write general expressions or *algorithms* for the processes shown above. For elimination of the ith variable x_i,

$$a_{kl} = a_{kl} \cdot a_{il}/a_{ii} \tag{3.2}$$

for $k = i+1, \ldots, n$ and $l = i+1, \ldots, n$

with $b_k = b_k - a_{ki} \cdot b_i/a_{ii}$ (3.3)

then $a_{ki} = 0$.

Note that,

(i) a_{ki} is not set to zero until the rest of the elimination is completed. This is important when this algorithm is considered to be applied as computer logic. In our mind we can store this coefficient, write zero (or a blank) on the work sheet and continue the elimination. In a computer program a_{ki} will be this store.

(ii) The algorithm will cease to operate when x_{n-1} has been eliminated. This will leave a final equation of the form,

$$a_{nn}x_n = b_n$$

which forms the start of the back substitution phase.

(iii) Expressions of the form of (3.2) and (3.3) are to be considered in the same way as assignment statements in a computer program. Thus the coefficient a_{kl} or b_k has an 'old' value which is inserted into the right-hand side of the expression to provide the 'new' value on the left-hand side.

The algorithms for the back substitution phase are

$$x_n = b_n / a_{nn} \tag{3.4}$$

and

$$x_i = \left(b_i - \sum_{j=i+1}^{j=n} a_{ij} x_j \right) / a_{ii} \tag{3.5}$$

for $i = n-1, \ldots, 1$

3.3 Computer programming implementation of Gaussian Elimination

Looking at algorithms (3.2) and (3.3) we see that only the coefficient matrix **A** and the vector **b** are involved in the elimination process. In a simple, efficient computer program the elimination is carried out on the variables within a two-dimensional array **A** and the one-dimensional array **b**. Thus **A** and **b** are successively changed row by row by applying the algorithms. The example below shows how **A** and **b** are changed for the example in Section 3.1. Note how coefficients in the lower half of **A** remain unchanged since we do not apply $a_{ki} = 0$. We shall see later that this is not required and may therefore be excluded from the process.

Example

For the example of Section 3.1

$$\mathbf{A} = \begin{bmatrix} 4 & 3 & 2 \\ 2 & 6 & 2 \\ 1 & 3 & 7 \end{bmatrix} \quad \text{and} \quad \mathbf{b} = \begin{bmatrix} 1 \\ 2 \\ 3 \end{bmatrix}$$

After the elimination of $\mathbf{x}_1$ the arrays become

$$\mathbf{A} = \begin{bmatrix} 4 & 3 & 2 \\ 2 & 4.5 & 1 \\ 1 & 2.25 & 6.5 \end{bmatrix} \quad \mathbf{b} = \begin{bmatrix} 1 \\ 1.5 \\ 2.75 \end{bmatrix}$$

After the elimination of $\mathbf{x}_2$ the arrays are

$$\mathbf{A} = \begin{bmatrix} 4 & 3 & 2 \\ 2 & 4.5 & 1 \\ 1 & 2.25 & 6 \end{bmatrix} \quad \mathbf{b} = \begin{bmatrix} 1 \\ 1.5 \\ 2 \end{bmatrix}$$

For the back substitution phase, only those elements of **A** above the solid line are required so that the setting $a_{ki} = 0$ is an unnecessary and time consuming action. To save storage and, to a certain extent, to avoid yet another array, the values of x_3, x_2, etc. are stored in **b** when they are computed. Thus,

$$b_n = x_n = b_n/a_{nn}$$

and $b_3 = x_3 = b_3/a_{33} = 2/6 = 0.3333$ and the back substitution steps are

(1) x_3 $\mathbf{A} = \begin{bmatrix} 4 & 3 & 2 \\ 2 & 4.5 & 1 \\ 1 & 2.25 & 6 \end{bmatrix}$ $\mathbf{b} = \begin{bmatrix} 1 \\ 1.5 \\ 0.3333 \end{bmatrix}$

(2) x_2 $\mathbf{A} = \begin{bmatrix} 4 & 3 & 2 \\ 2 & 4.5 & 1 \\ 1 & 2.25 & 6 \end{bmatrix}$ $\mathbf{b} = \begin{bmatrix} 1 \\ 0.259 \\ 0.333 \end{bmatrix}$

(3) x_1 $\mathbf{A} = \begin{bmatrix} 4 & 3 & 2 \\ 2 & 4.5 & 1 \\ 1 & 2.25 & 6 \end{bmatrix}$ $\mathbf{b} = \begin{bmatrix} -0.111 \\ 0.259 \\ 0.333 \end{bmatrix}$

Thus we see that the original forms of **A** and **b** are completely lost; an important consideration. An **x** vector is never required as the results are found in vector **b**.

Referring once again to algorithm (3.2), it can be seen that if $a_{ii} = 0$, division by zero would lead to an overflow error in a computer program. Usually this would mean that the coefficient matrix **A** is SINGULAR and the equations are linear combination of one another. However, in some situations and particularly in those equations set up for the Method of Tension Coefficients (see Chapter 4), zero diagonal values are present even in a solvable set of equations.

Thus a comprehensive program for Gaussian Elimination should contain a section for searching and swapping rows of **A** and **b**. If a_{kk} in row k is found to be zero then all subsequent rows $l = k + 1$ to n are investigated for $a_{lk} \neq 0$. When such a row is encountered this is swapped for row k, b_l is swapped for b_k and the elimination proceeds. If no such row can be found, the matrix of coefficients **A** is SINGULAR and no solution can be found.

3.4 Numerical integration

Although many of the functions to be integrated in elementary Structural Analysis are of a simple polynomial nature, numerical methods encoded into computer programs can remove the tedium of the calculations and the likelihood of error. The methods described below are approximate for one reason or another and therefore give approximate values to the definite integrals. Nevertheless, by using them with an increasing number of intervals or order, a number of significant figures can be determined which are sufficient for engineering purposes. Thus, most distances need only be measured to the nearest millimetre and in distances of the order of tens of metres, only five significant figures are required.

3.4.1 The composite trapezoidal rule

In one dimension, the region of integration L is divided into n equal intervals when $n+1$ ordinates or function values at the start and end of each interval (see Figure 3.1). Assuming the function is linear between each ordinate, the integral can be approximated to the sum of the areas of the n trapezia so formed. Thus,

$$I = \int_L f(x)\,dx \doteq \frac{L}{n}\left(\frac{f_1+f_2}{2} + \frac{f_2+f_3}{2} + \dots + \frac{f_{n-1}+f_n}{2} + \frac{f_n+f_{n+1}}{2}\right)$$

$$= \frac{L}{n}\left(\frac{f_1+f_{n+1}}{2} + \sum_{j=2}^{n} f_j\right) \tag{3.6}$$

where $f_j = f(x_j)$, the value of the function at the jth ordinate.

The integrated function may be two-dimensional or the product of functions. In the former case the region of integration in the

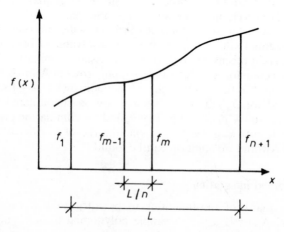

Figure 3.1

y–direction is also divided into equal intervals and the rule applied firstly in the x–direction for each y coordinate giving sub-integrals and then in the y–direction with each sub-integral. With the product of two functions, these need not be formally multiplied together since:

$$I = \int_L f(x).g(x)\,dx \doteq \frac{L}{n}\left(\frac{f_1 g_1 + f_{n+1}g_{n+1}}{2} + \sum_{j=2}^{n} f_j g_j\right) \quad (3.7)$$

Obviously the accuracy of the approximation is increased by increasing n.

3.4.2 The composite Simpson's rule

In the trapezoidal rule, the function is assumed to be a series of linear functions between ordinates. A higher order approximation would be to assume that the function is a parabola (second order polynomial) between ordinates. As Figure 3.3(a) shows, if this parabolic approximation covers two intervals and three ordinates, then the sub-integral is,

$$I_s = \int_{x_1}^{x_3} f(x)\,dx \doteq \frac{h}{3}(f_1 + 4f_2 + f_3)$$

where h is the interval length L/n. This will, of course, be exact if $f(x)$ is a second order polynomial.

For the composite rule (see Figure 3.2(b)), the complete integration range is divided into a series of these two interval parabolas and the

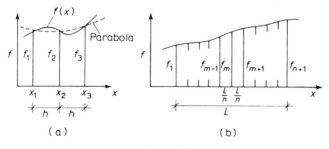

Figure 3.2

complete integral is:

$$I = \int_L f(x)\,dx \doteq \frac{L}{3n}\{f_1 + 4f_2 + f_3 + f_3 + 4f_4 + f_5 + \ldots + f_{n-1} + 4f_n + f_{n+1}\}$$

$$= \frac{L}{3n}\left\{f_1 + f_{n+1} + 4\sum_{j=2}^{n} \text{Even ordinates} + 2\sum_{j=3}^{n-1} \text{Odd ordinates}\right\}$$

(3.8)

Obviously, the number of intervals n must be an even number.

This rule may also be used with two-dimensional functions and products of functions in a similar way to the trapezoidal rule.

3.4.3 Gaussian quadrature

For a more complete theoretical background the reader is directed to reference [1], Section 2.6. In essence the method consists of evaluating the function at various special points X_i within the range of the integral and multiplying each such value by a special 'weighting' constant a_i. The integral is then given by:

$$I = \sum_{i=1}^{n} a_i f(X_i)$$

(3.9)

n, the order of integration, indicates the number of special points chosen and significantly, the integral will be 'exact' if $f(x)$ is a polynomial of order up to $2n-1$. Thus if $n=3$, the function is evaluated at only three special points and the integral is given by multiplying these three values by their respective weighting constants and adding them up. Furthermore, with just three function evaluations, the integral will be 'exact' for any function with up to x^5 terms! By 'exact' we mean that although in any numerical calculation some rounding off takes place, this will be very small.

The method thus has considerable computational advantages over the Trapezoidal and Simpson's rules since it involves fewer function evaluations. However, there is one small obstacle to overcome; the values of X_i and a_i are given only for integration over a range $X = -1$ to $X = +1$. Thus a simple transformation of the variable x must take place. For the integral,

$$I = \int_a^b f(x)\,dx$$

it can be shown that with

$$X = \frac{2x - (a+b)}{(b-a)},$$

$$I = \int_a^b f(x)\,dx = \frac{b-a}{2} \int_{-1}^{+1} f\left\{\frac{(b-a)X + (a+b)}{2}\right\} dX \qquad (3.10)$$

and the special points X_i and constants a_i can now be used. The following table gives these values for orders of integration up to 4:

Order n	X_i	a_i
1	0.0	2
2	± 0.577350269189	1.0
3	± 0.77489666924	0.55555555
	0.0	0.88888888
4	± 0.86113631159	0.34785484
	± 0.3399810435	0.6521451548

For higher orders, see reference [1], Section 2.6. Order 1 integration is of little use but $n=2$ and $n=3$ will usually be sufficient for the integrals encountered in elementary Structural Analysis. In these two cases:

$$I = \int_a^b f(x)\,dx \doteq \frac{b-a}{2}\left[1.0f\left(\frac{(b-a)X_1 + (a+b)}{2}\right) \right.$$
$$\left. + 1.0f\left(\frac{(b-a)X_2 + (a+b)}{2}\right) \right] \qquad (3.11)$$

where $X_1 = 0.577350269189$ and $X_2 = -0.577350269189$ for $n=2$ and

$$I = \int_a^b f(x)\,dx \doteq \frac{b-a}{2}\left[0.5555f\left(\frac{(b-a)X_1 + (a+b)}{2}\right) + \right.$$
$$\left. 0.8888f\left(\frac{a+b}{2}\right) + 0.5555f\left(\frac{(b-a)X_3 + (a+b)}{2}\right) \right] \qquad (3.12)$$

where $X_1 = 0.77459666924$, $X_2 = 0.0$ (assumed) and $X_3 = -0.77459666924$ for $n=3$.

The values of X_i and a_i are given to so many significant figures to enable the highest precision to be entered into the calculator or computer and hence reduce round off error.

WORKED EXAMPLES

Example 3.1 Gaussian Elimination with row swapping

Use the program shown below to solve:

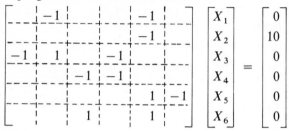

"SIMEQUAS"

```
10   HOME : PRINT "SOLUTION OF CM(N,N)*X(N)=P(N)": PRINT
12   PRINT "USING GAUSSIAN ELIMINATION WITH ROW SWAP": PRINT
14   INPUT "ORDER OF EQUATIONS (N) =";N: PRINT
15   DIM CM(N,N),P(N)
20   FOR I = 1 TO N
30   FOR J = 1 TO N
40   PRINT "ROW ";I;" COLUMN ";J;" ENTRY IN COEFFICIENT MATRIX ? ": PRINT

50   INPUT CM(I,J)
60   NEXT J: NEXT I
70   FOR I = 1 TO N
80   PRINT : PRINT "SUPPLY ENTRY ";I;" OF P VECTOR "
90   INPUT P(I)
100   NEXT I
110   GOSUB 5000
120   PRINT : PRINT "SOLUTION": PRINT
130   FOR I = 1 TO N
140   PRINT "P(";I;") = ";P(I)
150   NEXT I
160   END
5000 MG = N - 1
5010   DIM CS(N + 1)
5020   FOR IG = 1 TO MG
5030   IF CM(IG,IG) < > 0.0 THEN 5170
5040   FOR NG = IG + 1 TO N
5045 KG = NG
```

```
5050  IF CM(NG,IG) < > 0.0 THEN 5090
5060  IF NG < N THEN 5080
5070  PRINT "SINGULAR MATRIX-NO SOLUTION POSSIBLE !"
5080  NEXT NG
5090  FOR PG = IG TO N
5100  CS(PG) = CM(KG,PG)
5110  CM(KG,PG) = CM(IG,PG)
5120  CM(IG,PG) = CS(PG)
5130  NEXT PG
5140  CS(N + 1) = P(KG)
5150  P(KG) = P(IG)
5160  P(IG) = CS(N + 1)
5170  LG = IG + 1
5180  FOR JG = LG TO N
5190  IF CM(JG,IG) = 0.0 THEN 5240
5200  FOR KG = LG TO N
5210  CM(JG,KG) = CM(JG,KG) - CM(IG,KG) * CM(JG,IG) / CM(IG,IG)
5220  NEXT KG
5230  P(JG) = P(JG) - P(IG) * CM(JG,IG) / CM(IG,IG)
5240  NEXT JG
5250  NEXT IG
5260  P(N) = P(N) / CM(N,N)
5270  FOR IG = 1 TO MG
5280  KG = N - IG
5290  LG = KG + 1
5300  FOR JG = LG TO N
5310  P(KG) = P(KG) - P(JG) * CM(KG,JG)
5320  NEXT JG
5330  P(KG) = P(KG) / CM(KG,KG)
5340  NEXT IG
5350  RETURN
```

Program notes

(1) Line 14   In this case $N = 6$.
(2) Line 15   Arrays CM and P dimensioned after N is input.
(3) Line 80   Note, solution for X is returned in P, the right hand side vector.
(4) Line 5030   If the diagonal (IG) term is non-zero, computation continues normally from 5170.
(5) Lines 5040–5160   Row swapping. If a row with a non-zero value in the diagonal term cannot be found then a 'singular' warning is given (5050–5070).
(6) Lines 5170–5250   Elimination process.
(7) Lines 5260–5340   Back-substitution process.

The solution is $X_1 = 20$; $X_2 = 10$; $X_3 = 10$; $X_4 = -10$; $X_5 = -10$; $X_6 = -10$

Example 3.2 Numerical integration

Evaluate the integral

$$I = \int_{0}^{3} (x^2 + 2x + 3)(4x^2 + 5x + 6)\,dx$$

analytically and using the program listed below:

```
10  HOME : PRINT "NUMERICAL INTEGRATION OF F1*F2": PRINT
13  PRINT "USING SIMPSON'S RULE OR GAUSS QUADRATURE ": PRINT
16  PRINT "F1=AA*X^2+BB*X+CC": PRINT
18  PRINT "F2=PP*X^2+QQ*X+RR": PRINT
20  PRINT : PRINT "INPUT FUNCTION CONSTANTS": PRINT
30  INPUT "AA= ";AA: INPUT "BB= ";BB
40  INPUT "CC= ";CC: INPUT "PP= ";PP
50  INPUT "QQ= ";QQ: INPUT "RR= ";RR
53  PRINT : INPUT "LOWER LIMIT =";LI
57  PRINT : INPUT "UPPER LIMIT = ";LJ: PRINT
70  INPUT "GAUSS QUADRATURE ?";A$
80  IF A$ = "N" THEN 120
90  PRINT : INPUT "INTEGRATION ORDER (2 OR 3) = ";NG
100  GOSUB 6600
110  GOTO 130
120  PRINT : INPUT "NO OF INTERVALS FOR SIMPSON'S RULE = ";TT: PRINT
125  GOSUB 6400
130  PRINT : PRINT "AA= ";AA: PRINT "BB= ";BB: PRINT "CC= ";CC
140  PRINT "PP= ";PP: PRINT "QQ= ";QQ: PRINT "RR= ";RR
150  PRINT : PRINT "INTEGRAL VALUE = ";VI
160  PRINT : INPUT "TRY AGAIN WITH NEW METHOD OR FUNCTIONS (Y/N)";A$
170  PRINT : PRINT : IF A$ = "Y" THEN 20
180  END
6400  REM   SIMPSONS RULE-DOUBLE FUNCTION
6405  VI = 0.0
6410  IT = 2 * INT (0.5 * TT)
6420  IF TT = IT THEN 6450
6430  PRINT "ODD NO. OF INTERVALS-NUMBER INCREASED BY ONE"
6440  TT = TT + 1
6450  FI = (AA * LI * LI + BB * LI + CC) * (PP * LI * LI + QQ * LI + RR)
6460  LA = (AA * LJ * LJ + BB * LJ + CC) * (PP * LJ * LJ + QQ * LJ + RR)
6470  TI = (LJ - LI) / TT
```

```
6480 UI = - 1
6490 FOR IT = 1 TO TT - 1
6500 UI = - 1 * UI
6510 XX = LI + IT * TI
6520 VI = VI + (3 + UI) * (AA * XX * XX + BB * XX + CC) * (PP * XX * XX +
     QQ * XX + RR)
6530 NEXT IT
6540 VI = TI * (FI + LA + VI) / 3
6550 RETURN
6600 REM   2 OR 3 POINT GAUSS QUAD. NG=QUAD ORDER
6610 TD = 0.5 * (LJ - LI)
6620 TS = 0.5 * (LJ + LI)
6630 VI = 0.0
6640 IF NG = 3 THEN 6700
6650 TX = TD *  - 0.57735026919 + TS
6660 VI = VI + 1.0 * (AA * TX * TX + BB * TX + CC) * (PP * TX * TX + QQ *
     TX + RR)
6670 TX = TD * 0.57735026919 + TS
6680 VI = VI + 1.0 * (AA * TX * TX + BB * TX + CC) * (PP * TX * TX + QQ *
     TX + RR)
6684 VI = 0.5 * (LJ - LI) * VI
6690 RETURN
6700 TX = TD *  - 0.7745966624 + TS
6710 VI = VI + 0.55555555 * (AA * TX * TX + BB * TX + CC) * (PP * TX * TX
     + QQ * TX + RR)
6720 VI = VI + 0.88888888 * (AA * TS * TS + BB * TS + CC) * (PP * TS * TS
     + QQ * TS + RR)
6730 TX = TD * 0.7745966624 + TS
6740 VI = VI + 0.55555555 * (AA * TX * TX + BB * TX + CC) * (PP * TX * TX
     + QQ * TX + RR)
6745 VI = 0.5 * (LJ - LI) * VI
6750 RETURN
```

Program notes

(1) Lines 30–50   In this example AA = 1; BB = 2; CC = 3; PP = 4; QQ = 5; RR = 6.

(2) Line 70   If Gauss Quadrature not required then Simpson's Rule is used.

(3) Line 160   Integration may be repeated.

(4) Line 6440   If an odd number of intervals is specified, this is increased by one.

(5) Lines 6610, 6620, 6650, 6670   Variable transformation for use in Gauss Quadrature expression.

The analytical value of I is 885.15.
Values with 2-point Gauss Quadrature = 879.75 and
                    3-point Gauss Quadrature = 885.149986
Values with Simpson's Rule:
2 intervals, 893.25; 6 intervals, 885.25; 10 intervals, 885.16291; 14 intervals, 885.15337; 20 intervals, 885.15081.

PROBLEMS

(3.1) Swap the rows of **CM** and **P** in Example 3.1 before entering them into the program. Check that the solution remains unchanged.

(3.2) Set **CM**(1,2) in Example 3.1 to zero and attempt to solve the equations. Then starting with **CM**(1,2) = -10^{-10} carry out a series of runs with **CM**(1,2) made progressively smaller. At what point does the solution fail to satisfy the equations? This is the point at which the equations become 'ill-conditioned'. At what value of **CM**(1,2) is the 'Division by Zero' error indicated? This is the point at which the matrix **CM** becomes effectively singular on your computer.

(3.3) Alter the program in Example 3.1 to check that the solution satisfies the equations. The elements of **CM** must be stored in another array before entering the solution subroutine and this array premultiplies the solution vector to give a check on the original values of **P**.

(3.4) Change the solution subroutine of the program in Example 3.1 so that, firstly, two and then any number of **P** vectors can be processed in one call. **P** now becomes a two dimensional array, **P**($N,N1$) where $N1 = 2$ to start with. Thus the input section at lines 70–100 must be altered and the swapping section, lines 5100–5120, and lines 5230 and most of the back-substitution section must be changed to deal with $N1$ values of **P**.

(3.5) Is the array **CS**($N + 1$), line 5010, really necessary? Try to write a more compact form of the subroutine.

(3.6) Change the program given in Example 3.2 so that $F1$ and $F2$ are up to fourth order polynomials, i.e. $F1 = AAx^4 + BBx^3 + CCx^2 + C1x + C2$ and $F2 = PPx^4 + QQx^3 + RRx^2 + R1x + R2$.

(3.7) Using suitable limits and constants, and $F1$ and $F2$ as given in (3.6) above, test the accuracy of 2 and 3 point Gauss Quadrature with $PP = 0$ (i.e. $F1*F2$ is a 7th order polynomial) and $PP \neq 0$ (8th order polynomial). Reduce the order of $F1*F2$ by setting constants to zero and again observe the accuracy of the two orders of Quadrature. What changes should be made to increase the order of Quadrature to 4?

(3.8) Carry out a similar accuracy test to that given in (3.7) but using Simpson's Rule. Observe how many intervals are required to give reasonable accuracy and compare computation time with Gauss Quadrature.

(3.9) Substitute other functions for $F1$ and $F2$, i.e. $F1 = AA_*LOG(1+X)$ or $F2 = AA_*SIN(PI_*X/180)$ $(PI = \pi)$, etc. Compare the performance of Gauss Quadrature with Simpson's Rule.

Chapter 4

Forces analysis of trusses

ESSENTIAL THEORY

4.1 Representation of pin-jointed trusses

A pin-jointed truss is a skeletal structure whose members carry only axial forces either in tension or compression. The presence of pinned joints, which allow members to rotate independently of one another, ensures this. As the members cannot carry lateral loading by bending, their cross-sections are small and external loading must be applied only at joints.

Figure 4.1, shows typical representations of a pin-jointed truss with idealised supports. The straight lines represent the members and the circular joints indicate their pinned nature. Trusses with certain configurations carry the designer's name or a geometric description; two of these are shown in Figure 4.1

4.2 Supports

The loading on the truss is transferred through the structure to the supports where reactions develop. Actual supports may have a complex nature but we consider three idealized types shown in Figure 4.2

(a) Roller support. The frictionless pin and roller bearings allow complete freedom of rotation and translation tangentially to the support. Only a reaction normal to the support is therefore developed.

(b) Pinned support. Only freedom to rotate is permitted and the reaction is no longer normal to the support. Usually the reaction is defined by two mutually perpendicular components in the 'horizontal' and 'vertical' directions.

(c) Fixed support. Total fixity results in three components of the reaction. A moment is developed in addition to the two direct force components.

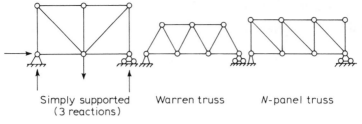

Simply supported   Warren truss   N-panel truss
(3 reactions)

Figure 4.1

Roller   Pinned   Fixed

R   ►H   ►H

Normal   Two components   M
reaction   of reaction   V

                         V   Three components
                                            of reaction

Figure 4.2

4.3 Statical determinancy

The aim of the analysis is to determine the forces in the members of the truss. The simplest methods of analysis use only the equations of static equilibrium. A truss or any other structure which can be analysed in this way is said to be STATICALLY DETERMINATE. If the equations of statics are insufficient for the analysis then the structure is said to be STATICALLY INDETERMINATE, REDUNDANT or HYPERSTATIC. We shall deal with statically determinate trusses in this chapter.

Frequently values of the reactions are required to initiate the analysis but in any case they will be required for checking purposes. To calculate these, the supports on the diagram are replaced by the appropriate reactions to give the Free Body Diagram (FBD). Considering the structure as a whole, the reaction components must be determined from the three equations of statical equilibrium discussed in the next section. Thus for a truss to be statically determinate, only three independent reactions can be present, the simplest support system for this condition is shown in Figure 4.1 and consists of a pinned and a roller support. A structure supported in this manner is said to be simply supported.

4.4 Equations of statical equilibrium

Although most structures are three dimensional it is usual to split them into plane, two-dimensional components for analysis purposes. The trusses drawn in Figure 4.1, are thus plane trusses. For a system of forces in two dimensions there are only three independent equations or conditions of equilibrium.

(1) The components of the forces in any direction must sum to zero.
(2) The sum of the components of the forces in another direction must be zero.
(3) The moments of the forces about any point in the plane must sum to zero.

Normally, the two directions chosen for force summation are at right angles and are generally the horizontal or x-direction and the vertical or y-direction. Thus, the equations may be summarised as

$$\Sigma F_x = 0; \ \Sigma F_y = 0 \text{ and } \Sigma M = 0$$

In the pin-jointed truss, the axial forces in the members meet at the joints or the supports. For coplanar forces meeting at a point only the first two conditions are required and this forms the basis of the methods described in this chapter.

If the truss has m members and b reactions, it can be seen that there are $m + b$ unknown forces to be computed. At each joint (including the supports) where coplanar forces meet, two independent equations of equilibrium may be established. Thus if there are j such joints and $2j = m + b$ then the truss will be statically determinate. Like most of such rules, this fails to identify those trusses which may be unstable and it should be used with caution. Nevertheless, the establishment of equilibrium equations at the joints of the truss is the basis of the two analytical methods now to be discussed.

4.5 Method of resolution at joints

Having calculated the reactions and drawn the free body diagram for the truss, the forces in the members may be found by applying the equations of equilibrium joint by joint. As only two equations may be set up at each joint, only those joints with at most two unknown member forces may be considered. If the truss is statically determinate then at least one such joint must exist at each stage of the analysis.

Three computational points should be noted:

(1) All unknown member forces are considered to be tensile (that is, 'pulling' on the joint). This is an arbitrary choice but is essential to maintain order in the calculations and aid checking. It has the

advantage that negative answers indicate that the member is in compression which is the usual sign convention.

(2) When moving to a new joint to evaluate more member forces, a member force 'pulling' on the previous joint will also be 'pulling' on the new joint. This is a reversal of the direction of action of the force without change of sign and arises from the equal and opposite forces applied to the ends of a member in tension.

(3) It is important that some check is made on the calculations. Usually one or more equations at the supports are not used in the analysis. These may be used as check equations for the determined member force values. This should be done even when a computer program is used since incorrect data may have been entered in an earlier part of the program.

4.5.1 Example

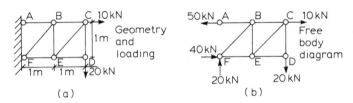

Figure 4.3

Calculation obviously starts at a joint with only two unknown forces. Although F is a reasonable choice, let us start at D and leave the supports for checking purposes.

JOINT D.

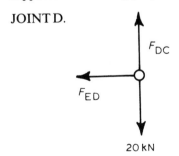

Note: F_{DC} and F_{ED} are assumed to be tensile.

Resolving forces vertically $20 - F_{DC} = 0$

$$F_{DC} = 20 \, \text{kN tensile}$$

Resolving forces horizontally $F_{ED} = 0$

We now move to a joint which has only two unknown forces, i.e.

JOINT C

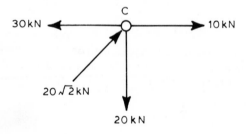

Note: F_{DC} is pulling down on joint C (but up on joint D), F_{BC} and F_{EC} are assumed to be in tension.

Resolving forces vertically $-20 - F_{EC} \sin 45° = 0$

therefore $\qquad F_{EC} = -20\sqrt{2} \text{ kN compression}$

Resolving forces horizontally $10 - F_{EC} \cos 45° - F_{BC} = 0$

therefore $\qquad 10 - (-20\sqrt{2}) . 1/\sqrt{2} - F_{BC} = 0$

therefore $\qquad F_{BC} = 30 \text{ kN tensile}$

Forces acting on Joint C are:

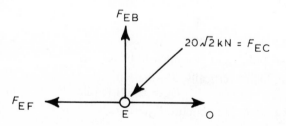

The next suitable joint is E

JOINT E

Note: F_{EC} is now pushing on joint E, F_{EB} and F_{EF} assumed tensile,

Resolving forces vertically $F_{EB} - 20\sqrt{2}.1/\sqrt{2} = 0$

therefore $F_{EB} = 20\,\text{kN}$ tensile

Resolving forces horizontally $0 - 20\sqrt{2}.1/\sqrt{2} - F_{FB} = 0$

$$F_{EF} = -20\,\text{kN} \text{ compression}$$

Forces acting on Joint E are

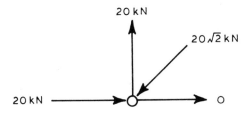

The final joint is B

JOINT B

F_{BC} and F_{EB} both 'pulling' on joint B. F_{AB} and F_{FB} assumed to be tensile.

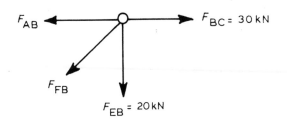

Resolving forces vertically $-20 - F_{FB} \sin 45° = 0$

$$F_{FB} = -20\sqrt{2}\,\text{kN} \text{ compressive}$$

Resolving forces horizontally $30 - F_{AB} + 20\sqrt{2} \cos 45° = 0$

$$F_{AB} = 50\,\text{kN} \text{ tensile}$$

Forces acting at Joint B

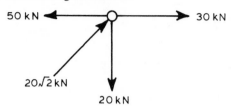

Checking forces with the reactions

The calculation proceeded from joint to joint until we reached one or both of the supports. By checking that the forces in those members connected to the supports are in equilibrium with the reactions, we are also providing a check on our calculations. This is by no means a foolproof check, as it is possible for two or more errors to cancel each other. However, this is quite rare and lack of equilibrium at this stage indicates an arithmetical or more fundamental error.

At support A

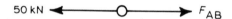

Resolving horizontally $50 - F_{AB} = 50 - 50 = 0 \checkmark$

At support F

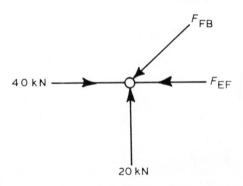

Resolving vertically $20 - F_{FB} \cdot 1/\sqrt{2} = 20 - 20\sqrt{2} \cdot 1/\sqrt{2} = 0 \checkmark$
Resolving horizontally $40 - F_{FB} - F_{FB} 1/\sqrt{2} = 40 - 20 - 20\sqrt{2} \cdot 1/$
$\sqrt{2} = 0 \checkmark$

4.6 General expression for unknown forces meeting at a point

Suppose n known forces $F_1, F_2, \ldots, F_n$ meet at a point each making an anticlockwise angle of $\alpha_1, \alpha_2, \ldots, \alpha_n$ ($0 < \alpha < 360°$) to the reference axis (the horizontal axis in this case).

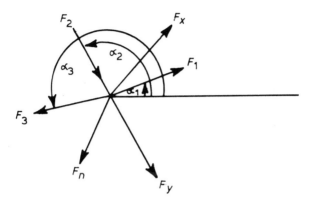

If the two unknown forces are F_x and F_y making anticlockwise angles α_x and α_u to the horizontal, then resolving horizontally

$$\sum_{i=1}^{n} F_i \cos \alpha_i + F_x \cos \alpha_x + F_y \cos \alpha_y = 0$$

and resolving vertically

$$\sum_{i=1}^{n} F_i \sin \alpha_i + F_x \sin \alpha_x + F_y \sin \alpha_y = 0$$

In these expressions it should be noted that F_i are assumed to be tensile positive forces, i.e. pulling on the point and $\cos \alpha_i$ and $\sin \alpha_i$ assume the appropriate signs for the given quadrant.

Solving the above equations for F_x and F_y, gives the following expressions,

$$F_x = \frac{\left(\sum_{i=1}^{n} F_i \sin \alpha_i\right) \cos \alpha_y - \left(\sum_{i=1}^{n} F_i \cos \alpha_i\right) \sin \alpha_y}{(\cos \alpha_x \sin \alpha_y - \sin \alpha_x \cos \alpha_y)}$$

$$F_y = \frac{\left(\sum_{i=1}^{n} F_i \sin \alpha_i\right) \cos \alpha_x - \left(\sum_{i=1}^{n} F_i \cos \alpha_i\right) \sin \alpha_x}{(\cos \alpha_y \sin \alpha_x - \sin \alpha_y \cos \alpha_x)} \qquad (4.1)$$

which will be used in various computer programs to carry out this method of resolution at joints.

4.7 The method of tension coefficients

This method consists of assembling sufficient joint equilibrium equations and solving them simultaneously to give the force in each member. If there are N members then N equations are required.

The method avoids the problem of finding a joint with only two unknown forces. It does have the disadvantage of requiring the solution of a set of simultaneous equations which may put it beyond hand calculation.

The *tension coefficient* t of a member is the tensile force per unit length of the member (a negative value indicating compression) and the simultaneous equilibrium equations are usually written in terms of such quantities for reasons that will be explained.

The equilibrium equations for member forces meeting at a joint I, shown below, can be expressed in terms of tension coefficients as follows.

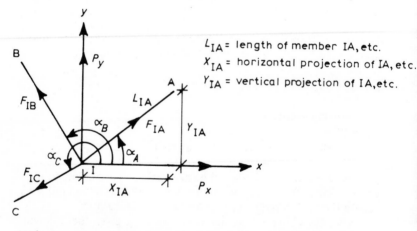

L_{IA} = length of member IA, etc.

X_{IA} = horizontal projection of IA, etc.

Y_{IA} = vertical projection of IA, etc.

All forces assumed to be in tension. P_x and P_u are applied joint loads.
    Resolving in x-direction.

$$P_x + F_{IA} \cos \alpha_A + F_{IB} \cos \alpha_B + F_{IC} \cos \alpha_C = 0$$

$$\therefore \quad P_x + F_{IA}\frac{X_{IA}}{L_{IA}} + F_{IB}\frac{X_{IB}}{L_{IB}} + F_{IC}\frac{X_{IC}}{L_{IC}} = 0$$

$$\therefore \quad P_x + X_{IA}t_{IA} + X_{IB}t_{IB} + X_{IC}t_{IC} = 0$$

or

$$X_{IA}t_{IA} + X_{IB}t_{IB} + X_{IC}t_{IC} = -P_x$$

The horizontal force exerted on the joint by a member is equal to its tension coefficient multiplied by the horizontal projection of the member. Note that for members IB and IC as shown, the horizontal projections are negative and this is consistent with the signs of $\cos \alpha_B$ and $\cos \alpha_C$.

Resolving in the y-direction.

$$P_y + F_{1A} \sin \alpha_A + F_{1B} \sin \alpha_B + F_{1C} \sin \alpha_C = 0$$

$$\therefore \quad P_y + F_{1A} \frac{Y_{1A}}{L_{1A}} + F_{1B} \frac{Y_{1B}}{L_{1B}} + F_{1C} \frac{Y_{1C}}{L_{1C}} = 0$$

$$\therefore \quad Y_{1A} t_{1A} + Y_{1B} t_{1B} + Y_{1C} t_{1C} = -P_y$$

and the vertical force exerted on the joint by a member is equal to the tension coefficient multiplied by the vertical projection of the member. In this case Y_{1C} is negative.

The simplicity of these equations accounts for the use of tension coefficients in such hand calculations as are possible. In drawing a truss in the first place, the coordinates of the joints are required from which the projections of the members are readily obtained. The positive directions of the coordinates axes are arbitrary but must be the same for each joint. In the analysis of the truss shown in the previous section we set up sufficient of such equations to solve for all the forces in the members. Figure 4.4 shows that there are eight members and for clarity, the panels are taken to be of length l and height h.

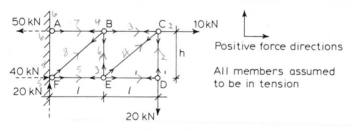

Figure 4.4

As we need a total of eight equilibrium equations (containing the eight unknown forces) which are to be solved simultaneously, we need not and cannot be restricted to joints with only two unknown forces. Thus the two equations at each joint D, C, E and B will be sufficient but equations at A and F should be used for checking purposes. The positive directions of forces are shown in the figure and these axes may be assumed to be attached to the particular joint under consideration. As we move from joint to joint, these directions should not be changed. All members are assumed to be in tension and the direction of action of the forces on each joint is shown. These will be positive or negative according to the chosen force direction axes. Thus, assembling the equations of equilibrium using tension coefficients:

JOINT D

$\rightarrow \quad -l.t_{DE} \qquad\qquad\qquad =0$

$\uparrow \quad h.t_{CD}-20 \qquad\qquad\quad =0$

JOINT C

$\rightarrow \quad -l.t_{BC}-l.t_{CE}+10 \qquad =0$

$\uparrow \quad -h.t_{CD}-h.t_{CE} \qquad\quad =0$

JOINT E

$\rightarrow \quad l.t_{DE}+l.t_{CE}-l.t_{EF} \qquad =0$

$\uparrow \quad h.t_{BE}+h.t_{CE} \qquad\qquad =0$

JOINT B

$\rightarrow \quad -l.t_{AB}+l.t_{BC}-l.t_{BF} \qquad =0$

$\uparrow \quad -h.t_{BE}-h.t_{BF} \qquad\qquad =0$

Check through these equations to make sure you understand how the negative signs arise.

The equations may be written in matrix form,

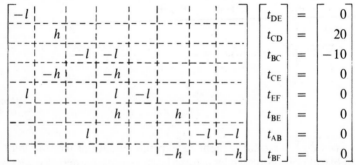

Note that:

(1) The 'right-hand side' or 'load' vector contains the applied load components. The signs are reversed since the components have been transferred to the other side of the equation.

(2) In this case there is an entry in every diagonal element of the coefficient matrix. This is not always necessarily so as it depends on

the lettering of joints and the order in which the tension coefficients are listed in the vector of 'unknowns'. Hence if a Gaussian Elimination subroutine is used to solve these equations, it should contain a row swapping facility (see Example 3.1).

Taking $h = 1$ m and $l = 1$ m gives the solution

$$t_{DE} = 0 \qquad t_{CD} = 20 \text{ kN/m} \qquad t_{BC} = 30 \text{ kN/m}$$

$$t_{CE} = -20 \text{ kN/m} \qquad t_{EF} = -20 \text{ kN/m} \qquad t_{BE} = 20 \text{ kN/m}$$

$$t_{AB} = 50 \text{ N/m} \qquad t_{BF} = -20 \text{ kN/m}$$

The equations at joints A and F are used to check these values.

JOINT A

$\rightarrow \quad 1.t_{AB} - 50 = 0 \checkmark$

JOINT F

$\rightarrow \quad 1.t_{FE} + 1.t_{FB} + 40 = 0 \checkmark$

$\uparrow \quad 20 + 1.t_{BF} = 0 \checkmark$

Again, this check is not totally foolproof but is useful.

The forces are calculated by multiplying the tension coefficients by the lengths of the members.

$$F_{DE} = 0$$

$$F_{BC} = 1.30 = 30 \text{ kN (tension)}$$

$$F_{EF} = 1. -20 = -20 \text{ kN (compression)}$$

$$F_{AB} = 1.50 = 50 \text{ kN (tension)}$$

$$F_{CD} = 1.20 = 20 \text{ kN (tension)}$$

$$F_{CE} = \sqrt{2}. -20 = -20\sqrt{2} \text{ kN (compression)}$$

$$F_{BE} = 1.20 = 20 \text{ kN (tension)}$$

$$F_{BF} = \sqrt{2}. -20 = -20\sqrt{2} \text{ kN (compression)}$$

4.8 The method of sections

Not only are the forces in the members of a truss in equilibrium at the joints but also the forces acting on an isolated portion or section of the structure must also be in equilibrium. Thus, imagine cutting vertically through members AB, FB and FE of the structure shown in Figure 4.4 and isolating the two parts of the structure so formed. If members are to remain in their original orientations forces must be applied to either side of the cut to maintain equilibrium of the two parts. These forces are the forces which develop in the cut members due to the applied loading and are equal and opposite on either side of the cut. If this was not so then a resultant external force at the cut would develop when the two parts are put together. Figure 4.5 illustrates this imaginary process.

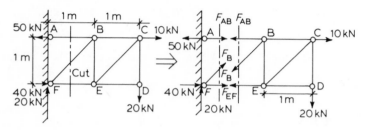

Figure 4.5

Equilibrium equations can be set up for each isolated part of the structure and if there are no more than three unknown forces, a solution of these equations can be found.

Consider the right-hand isolated part BCDE of the structure shown

Resolving vertically, $-F_{BF} \cos 45° - 20 = 0$

$$F_{BF} = -20\sqrt{2}\,\text{kN (compression)}$$

Moments about B, $F_{EF}.1 + 20.1 = 0$

$$F_{EF} = -20\,\text{kN (compression)}$$

Resolving horizontally,

$$-F_{AB} - F_{BF} \cos 45° - F_{EF} + 10 = 0$$

$$F_{AB} = 10 + 20\sqrt{2}/\sqrt{2} + 20 = 50\,\text{kN (tension)}$$

Considering equilibrium of the left-hand part, AF, of the truss, these results can be obtained more quickly.

The method of sections is not readily adaptable to programming but is an important aide to checking computer output. With a little practice you will be able to consider sections mentally and at least determine whether a member is in tension or compression. Frequently the force values can be determined with little or no written computation.

WORKED EXAMPLES

Example 4.1 Resolution at joints

Use the program listed below to find the force in each member of the pin-jointed truss shown in Figure 4.3.

```
10  REM  MEMBER FORCES BY RESOLUTION AT JOINTS
15  DIM F(20),A(20)
20  HSUM = 0.0
25  VSUM = 0.0
30  PI = 4 *  ATN (1.0)
32  HOME
33  PRINT
34  PRINT "TRUSS MEMBER FORCES"
35  PRINT
36  PRINT "BY RESOLUTION AT JOINTS"
37  PRINT
38  INPUT "FORCE UNITS ? ";F$
40  PRINT
45  PRINT "FORCE UNITS ARE ";F$
50  PRINT
55  INPUT "NO OF FORCES MEETING AT JOINT ? ";N
60  PRINT
65  PRINT "NO OF FORCES MEETING AT JOINT = ";N
70  PRINT
72  INPUT "NO OF UNKNOWN FORCES (1 OR 2) ?";NU: PRINT
75 NN = N - NU
80  FOR I = 1 TO NN
85  PRINT
90  PRINT "MAGITUDE OF KNOWN FORCE ";I
92  PRINT "(TENSILE ACTION POSITIVE)"
95  INPUT F(I)
100  PRINT
105  PRINT "ANTI CLOCKWISE ANGLE OF ACTION (DEGREES)"
110  INPUT A(I)
115 HSUM = HSUM + F(I) *  COS (PI * A(I) / 180)
120 VSUM = VSUM + F(I) *  SIN (PI * A(I) / 180)
125  NEXT I
130  PRINT
135  PRINT "SUMMARY OF KNOWN FORCES "
140  PRINT
145  PRINT "MAGNITUDE","ANGLE"
147  PRINT "  ";F$
150  PRINT
155  FOR I = 1 TO NN
160  PRINT F(I),A(I)
165  PRINT
```

```
170   NEXT I
173   PRINT : INPUT "ANY CHANGES Y/N ?";A$: IF A$ = "N" THEN 178
175   HSUM = 0.0:VSUM = 0.0: GOTO 50
178   PRINT
180   PRINT "ANTICLOCKWISE ANGLE OF ACTION"
182   PRINT "OF FIRST UNKNOWN FORCE "
185   INPUT ALPHA
188   PRINT
189   IF NU = 1 THEN 198
190   PRINT "ANTICLOCKWISE ANGLE OF ACTION"
192   PRINT "OF SECOND UNKNOWN FORCE"
195   INPUT BETA
198   A1 = PI * ALPHA / 180
200   A2 = PI * BETA / 180
205   F1 = (VSUM *  COS (A2) - HSUM *  SIN (A2)) / ( COS (A1) *  SIN (A2) -
       SIN (A1) *  COS (A2))
207   IF NU = 1 THEN 215
210   F2 = (VSUM *  COS (A1) - HSUM *  SIN (A1)) / ( COS (A2) *  SIN (A1) -
       SIN (A2) *  COS (A1))
215   PRINT
218   A1 = 180 * A1 / PI
220   PRINT "FIRST UNKNOWN FORCE = ";F1;F$;" AT ";A1;" DEGREES ANTICLOCKWI
       SE TO REFERENCE"
225   PRINT
227   IF NU = 1 THEN 235
228   A2 = 180 * A2 / PI
230   PRINT "SECOND UNKNOWN FORCE = ";F2;F$;" AT ";A2;" DEGREES ANTICLOCKW
       ISE TO REFERENCE"
235   PRINT : INPUT "PRESS RETURN TO CONTINUE";B$
238   HOME
240   PRINT
245   PRINT "SUMMARY OF FORCES ACTING AT JOINT"
250   PRINT
255   PRINT "TENSILE POSITIVE"
260   PRINT
265   PRINT
270   PRINT "FORCE","ANGLE(DEGS)"
272   PRINT " ";F$
275   PRINT
280   FOR I = 1 TO NN
285   PRINT F(I),A(I)
290   PRINT
295   NEXT I
300   PRINT F1,ALPHA
305   PRINT
308   IF NU = 1 THEN 320
310   PRINT F2,BETA
```

```
315  PRINT
320  PRINT
325  INPUT "DO YOU WISH TO CONSIDER ANOTHER JOINT ?";B$
330  IF B$ = "N" THEN 340
332  HSUM = 0.0:VSUM = 0.0
335  HOME : GOTO 50
340  END
```

Program notes

(1) This program finds the one or two unknown forces of a set of forces meeting at a joint using Equation (4.1). The choice of joint is left to the user who must remember to reverse the direction of forces when moving to a new joint.

(2) Lines 50–125 Self-explanatory input of known forces and directions for a particular joint. These are summarised (130–170) and changes can be made (173–178).

(3) Lines 180–210 Input of unknown force directions and calculation of magnitudes F1 and F2 (205–210).

(4) Lines 210–340   Print out of results.

Typically, for the first four joints:

```
TRUSS MEMBER FORCES

BY RESOLUTION AT JOINTS

FORCE UNITS ? KN

FORCE UNITS ARE KN

NO OF FORCES MEETING AT JOINT ? 3

NO OF FORCES MEETING AT JOINT = 3

NO OF UNKNOWN FORCES (1 OR 2) ?2

MAGITUDE OF KNOWN FORCE 1
(TENSILE ACTION POSITIVE)
?20

ANTI CLOCKWISE ANGLE OF ACTION (DEGREES)
?270

SUMMARY OF KNOWN FORCES

MAGNITUDE         ANGLE
   KN

20                270


ANY CHANGES Y/N ?N

ANTICLOCKWISE ANGLE OF ACTION
OF FIRST UNKNOWN FORCE
?90
```

```
ANTICLOCKWISE ANGLE OF ACTION
OF SECOND UNKNOWN FORCE
?180
```

FIRST UNKNOWN FORCE = 20KN AT 90 DEGREES ANTICLOCKWISE TO REFERENCE

SECOND UNKNOWN FORCE = OKN AT 180 DEGREES ANTICLOCKWISE TO REFERENCE

PRESS RETURN TO CONTINUE

SUMMARY OF FORCES ACTING AT JOINT

TENSILE POSITIVE

FORCE KN	ANGLE(DEGS)
20	270
20	90
0	180

DO YOU WISH TO CONSIDER ANOTHER JOINT ?Y

NO OF FORCES MEETING AT JOINT ? 4

NO OF FORCES MEETING AT JOINT = 4

NO OF UNKNOWN FORCES (1 OR 2) ?2

```
MAGITUDE OF KNOWN FORCE 1
(TENSILE ACTION POSITIVE)
?10
```

```
ANTI CLOCKWISE ANGLE OF ACTION (DEGREES)
?0
```

```
MAGITUDE OF KNOWN FORCE 2
(TENSILE ACTION POSITIVE)
?20
```

```
ANTI CLOCKWISE ANGLE OF ACTION (DEGREES)
?270
```

SUMMARY OF KNOWN FORCES

MAGNITUDE KN	ANGLE
10	0
20	270

ANY CHANGES Y/N ?N

```
ANTICLOCKWISE ANGLE OF ACTION
OF FIRST UNKNOWN FORCE
?180
```

```
ANTICLOCKWISE ANGLE OF ACTION
OF SECOND UNKNOWN FORCE
?225
```

FIRST UNKNOWN FORCE = 30KN AT 180 DEGREES ANTICLOCKWISE TO REFERENCE

SECOND UNKNOWN FORCE = -28.2842713KN AT 225 DEGREES ANTICLOCKWISE TO REFERENCE

PRESS RETURN TO CONTINUE

SUMMARY OF FORCES ACTING AT JOINT

```
TENSILE POSITIVE

FORCE              ANGLE(DEGS)
  KN

10                 0

20                 270

30                 180

-28.2842713        225


DO YOU WISH TO CONSIDER ANOTHER JOINT ?N
```

Example 4.2 Member forces using tension coefficients

The program below enables the user to set up joint by joint, sufficient tension coefficient equilibrium equations to solve for all tension coefficients and forces in the members of a pin-jointed truss. Members (and joints) are numbered in an arbitrary manner and member lengths form the data. Use the program to find the forces in the truss shown in Figure 4.3.

```
10  DIM CM(20,20),P(20),LE(20)
20  HOME
25  PRINT "TRUSS ANALYSIS BY TENSION COEFFICIENT": PRINT : PRINT "METHOD-
    USER ASSEMBLES EQUATIONS": PRINT
28  PRINT : PRINT "GIVE EACH MEMBER A NUMBER CONSEC FROM 1": PRINT
30  PRINT "CALCULATE LENGTHS,ASSEMBLE SUFFICIENT": PRINT
35  PRINT "EQUATIONS IN ANY ORDER USING CONSISTENT": PRINT
38  PRINT "AXES. PROGRAM WILL DIRECT INPUT FOR": PRINT
40  PRINT "MATRIX ASSEMBLY,SOLVE EQUATIONS AND": PRINT
45  PRINT "CALCULATE FORCES": PRINT
50  INPUT "NUMBER OF MEMBERS IN TRUSS ?";NM
60  PRINT
65  INPUT "FORCE UNITS,N OR KN ?";F$: PRINT : INPUT "LENGTH UNITS,M OR MM
      ?";L$: PRINT
70  FOR J = 1 TO NM
80  PRINT "LENGTH OF MEMBER NO ";J;"?"
90  INPUT LE(J)
100  PRINT
110  NEXT J
120  FOR I = 1 TO NM
130  PRINT "ASSEMBLING EQUATION NO ";I
140  PRINT
150  PRINT "NUMBER OF MEMBER MEETING AT JOINT ": INPUT "(-VE NO ENDS COEF
     FICIENT INPUT) ?";J
151  PRINT : PRINT
160  IF J < 0 THEN 230
```

```
170  PRINT : INPUT "PROJECTION OF MEMBER LENGTH ?";PR: PRINT
180 CM(I,J) = PR
190  GOTO 150
200  IF J < 0 THEN 230
210 CM(I,J) = PR
220  GOTO 150
230  INPUT "FORCE COMPONENT (ZERO IF NONE) ?";F
240  PRINT
250  P(I) =  - F
260  NEXT I
270  PRINT
280  PRINT "****** PROCEEDING TO SOLUTION ******"
290  PRINT
300  PRINT
305 N = NM
310  GOSUB 5000
320  PRINT
330  HOME : PRINT
340  PRINT
350  PRINT "MEMBER"; TAB( 10);"TEN.COEFF."; TAB( 25);"FORCE"
360  PRINT  TAB( 10);" (";F$;"/";L$;")"; TAB( 25);" (";F$;")": PRINT
370  FOR I = 1 TO NM
380  PRINT  TAB( 3);I; TAB( 10);P(I); TAB( 25);LE(I) * P(I): NEXT I
390  END
470  END
5000 MG = N - 1
5010  DIM CS(N + 1)
5020  FOR IG = 1 TO MG
5030  IF CM(IG,IG) < > 0.0 THEN 5170
5040  FOR NG = IG + 1 TO N
5045 KG = NG
5050  IF CM(NG,IG) < > 0.0 THEN 5090
5060  IF NG < N THEN 5080
5070  PRINT "SINGULAR MATRIX-NO SOLUTION POSSIBLE !"
5080  NEXT NG
5090  FOR PG = IG TO N
5100 CS(PG) = CM(KG,PG)
5110 CM(KG,PG) = CM(IG,PG)
5120 CM(IG,PG) = CS(PG)
5130  NEXT PG
5140 CS(N + 1) = P(KG)
5150 P(KG) = P(IG)
5160 P(IG) = CS(N + 1)
5170 LG = IG + 1
5180  FOR JG = LG TO N
5190  IF CM(JG,IG) = 0.0 THEN 5240
```

```
5200   FOR KG = LG TO N
5210   CM(JG,KG) = CM(JG,KG) - CM(IG,KG) * CM(JG,IG) / CM(IG,IG)
5220   NEXT KG
5230   P(JG) = P(JG) - P(IG) * CM(JG,IG) / CM(IG,IG)
5240   NEXT JG
5250   NEXT IG
5260   P(N) = P(N) / CM(N,N)
5270   FOR IG = 1 TO MG
5280   KG = N - IG
5290   LG = KG + 1
5300   FOR JG = LG TO N
5310   P(KG) = P(KG) - P(JG) * CM(KG,JG)
5320   NEXT JG
5330   P(KG) = P(KG) / CM(KG,KG)
5340   NEXT IG
5350   RETURN
```

Program notes

(1) Lines 10–110   Data input. NM is number of members.
(2) Lines 120–260   Setting up equilibrium equations. NM equations are formed using data presented by the user; number of members meeting at joint and its projection and the force applied at the joint. Thus the user chooses joint and the direction of resolution of forces.

Typical (but shortened) run for truss shown in Figure 4.3 is shown below. Note that member numbers are DE = 1; CD = 2; BC = 3; CE = 4; EF = 5; EB = 6; AB = 7 and BF = 8. The axes chosen are x positive to the *left* and y positive upwards.

```
TRUSS ANALYSIS BY TENSION C EFFICIENT

METHOD-USER ASSEMBLES EQUATIONS


GIVE EACH MEMBER A NUMBER CONSEC FROM 1

CALCULATE LENGTHS,ASSEMBLE SUFFICIENT

EQUATIONS IN ANY ORDER USING CONSISTENT

AXES. PROGRAM WILL DIRECT INPUT FOR

MATRIX ASSEMBLY,SOLVE EQUATIONS AND

CALCULATE FORCES

NUMBER OF MEMBERS IN TRUSS ?8

FORCE UNITS,N OR KN ?KN

LENGTH UNITS,M OR MM ?M
```

```
LENGTH OF MEMBER NO 1?
?1

LENGTH OF MEMBER NO 2?
?1

LENGTH OF MEMBER NO 3?
?1

LENGTH OF MEMBER NO 4?
?1.414

LENGTH OF MEMBER NO 5?
?1

LENGTH OF MEMBER NO 6?
?1

LENGTH OF MEMBER NO 7?
?1

LENGTH OF MEMBER NO 8?
?1.414

ASSEMBLING EQUATION NO 1

NUMBER OF MEMBER MEETING AT JOINT
(-VE NO ENDS COEFFICIENT INPUT) ?1


PROJECTION OF MEMBER LENGTH ?1

NUMBER OF MEMBER MEETING AT JOINT
(-VE NO ENDS COEFFICIENT INPUT) ?-1

FORCE COMPONENT (ZERO IF NONE) ?0

ASSEMBLING EQUATION NO 2

NUMBER OF MEMBER MEETING AT JOINT
(-VE NO ENDS COEFFICIENT INPUT) ?2


PROJECTION OF MEMBER LENGTH ?1

NUMBER OF MEMBER MEETING AT JOINT
(-VE NO ENDS COEFFICIENT INPUT) ?-1

FORCE COMPONENT (ZERO IF NONE) ?-20

ASSEMBLING EQUATION NO 3

NUMBER OF MEMBER MEETING AT JOINT
(-VE NO ENDS COEFFICIENT INPUT) ?3


PROJECTION OF MEMBER LENGTH ?1

NUMBER OF MEMBER MEETING AT JOINT
(-VE NO ENDS COEFFICIENT INPUT) ?4
```

```
PROJECTION OF MEMBER LENGTH ?1

NUMBER OF MEMBER MEETING AT JOINT
(-VE NO ENDS COEFFICIENT INPUT) ?-1

FORCE COMPONENT (ZERO IF NONE) ?-10

ASSEMBLING EQUATION NO 4

NUMBER OF MEMBER MEETING AT JOINT
(-VE NO ENDS COEFFICIENT INPUT) ?2

PROJECTION OF MEMBER LENGTH ?-1

NUMBER OF MEMBER MEETING AT JOINT
(-VE NO ENDS COEFFICIENT INPUT) ?4
```

(A section of output has been removed here.)

MEMBER	TEN.COEFF. (KN/M)	FORCE (KN)
1	0	0
2	20	20
3	30	30
4	-20	-28.28
5	-20	-20
6	20	20
7	50	50
8	-20	-28.28

Example 4.3 Tension coefficient method

Again, calculate the forces in the members of the truss shown in Figure 4.3 using the following program. This program calculates the member projections, where required, from the coordinates of the joints and requires, in addition, a 'positive' and 'negative' end joint number for each member. Thus joints as well as members are arbitrarily numbered and each member has an arbitrarily chosen positive and negative end with corresponding joint number. Usually an arrow is drawn on the member to indicate these ends; head $(+)$, tail $(-)$. This is the form of the data required in more advanced programs for statically indeterminate structures.

```
5  HOME : PRINT : PRINT "ANALYSIS OF TRUSS BY METHOD OF": PRINT "TENSION
      COEFFICIENTS": PRINT
10  DIM X(20),Y(20),EP(20),EN(20),PX(20),PY(20),LE(20),P(20),CM(20,20)
20  PRINT : INPUT "NO OF MEMBERS IN TRUSS ?";NM: PRINT
30  INPUT "NO OF JOINTS (INCLUDING SUPPORTS) ?";NJ: PRINT
35  INPUT "FORCE UNITS,N OR KN ?";F$: PRINT
40  FOR I = 1 TO NJ
```

```
50   PRINT "X-COORD OF JOINT ";I: INPUT X(I)
60   PRINT : PRINT "Y-COORD OF JOINT ";I: INPUT Y(I): PRINT
70   PRINT : INPUT "X-DIRN COMP OF LOADING ?";PX(I): PRINT
80   INPUT "Y-DIRN COMP OF LOADING ?";PY(I): PRINT : NEXT I
90   FOR I = 1 TO NM
100  PRINT "POSITIVE END JOINT NO FOR MEMBER ";I: INPUT EP(I): PRINT
110  PRINT "NEGATIVE END JOINT NO FOR MEMBER ";I: INPUT EN(I): PRINT : NEXT
     I
120  HOME : PRINT : PRINT "DATA SUMMARY": PRINT
130  PRINT "JOINT COORDINATES": PRINT : PRINT "JOINT"; TAB( 10);"X-COORD"
     ; TAB( 25);"Y-COORD": PRINT
140  FOR I = 1 TO NJ: PRINT  TAB( 3);I; TAB( 10);X(I); TAB( 25);Y(I): NEXT
     I
150  PRINT : INPUT "PRESS RETURN TO CONTINUE";A$
160  HOME : PRINT : PRINT "JOINT LOADING": PRINT
170  PRINT "JOINT"; TAB( 10);"X=DIRN(";F$;")"; TAB( 25);"Y-DIRN(";F$;")":
     PRINT
180  FOR I = 1 TO NJ: PRINT  TAB( 3);I; TAB( 10);PX(I); TAB( 25);PY(I): NEXT
     I
190  PRINT : INPUT "PRESS RETURN TO CONTINUE";A$
200  HOME : PRINT : PRINT "MEMBER END JOINT NUMBERS": PRINT
210  PRINT "MEMBER"; TAB( 10);"+VE END"; TAB( 20);"-VE END": PRINT
220  FOR I = 1 TO NM: PRINT  TAB( 3);I; TAB( 10);EP(I); TAB( 20);EN(I): NEXT
     I
230  PRINT : INPUT "ANY ERRORS ? TRY AGAIN ? Y/N ";A$
240  IF A$ = "Y" THEN 20
250  HOME : PRINT : PRINT "BUILD UP TENSION COEFFICIENT EQUATIONS": PRINT
     "JOINT BY JOINT"
255  R = 0:R1 = 0
260  PRINT : PRINT : INPUT "JOINT NO ?";I:FI = 0:R = R + 1: IF 2 * R - 1 -
     R1 > NM THEN 510
270  PRINT : INPUT "IS JOINT RESTRAINED Y/N ?";A$: PRINT : IF A$ = "N" THEN
     290
280  INPUT "IN X-DIRN (1) OR Y-DIRN (2) ?";FI
290  PRINT : PRINT "NO OF MEMBERS MEETING AT JOINT ";I: INPUT NO
300  FOR II = 1 TO NO: IF II > 1 THEN 320
310  PRINT : INPUT "FIRST MEMBER NO ?";J: GOTO 330
320  PRINT : INPUT "NEXT MEMBER NO ?";J: PRINT
330 K = EP(J):L = EN(J):HP = X(K) - X(L): IF I = K THEN HP =  - HP
340 VP = Y(K) - Y(L): IF I = K THEN VP =  - VP
350 LE(J) =  SQR (HP * HP + VP * VP)
360  IF FI > 0 THEN 390
370 CM(2 * R - 1 - R1,J) = HP: IF 2 * R - 1 - R1 = NM THEN 410
380 CM(2 * R - R1,J) = VP: GOTO 410
```

```
390 V = HP: IF FI = 1 THEN V = VP
400 CM(2 * R - 1 - R1,J) = V
410  NEXT II
420  IF FI = 0 THEN 460
430  IF FI = 1 THEN 450
440 P(2 * R - R1 - 1) = - PX(I):R1 = R1 + 1: GOTO 490
450 P(2 * R - R1 - 1) = - PY(I):R1 = R1 + 1: GOTO 490
460 P(2 * R - R1 - 1) = - PX(I): IF 2 * R - R1 - 1 < NM THEN 480
470  PRINT : PRINT "ENOUGH EQUATIONS-PROCEEDING TO SOLVE": PRINT : GOTO 5
     20
480 P(2 * R - R1) = - PY(I)
490  PRINT : INPUT "ANY MORE JOINTS ?";A$: IF A$ = "Y" THEN 260
500  PRINT : PRINT "PROCEEDING TO SOLVE EQUATIONS ": PRINT : GOTO 520
510  PRINT : PRINT "NO MORE JOINTS REQUIRED-SOLVING !": PRINT
520 N = NM: GOSUB 5000
530 HOME : PRINT : PRINT "MEMBER FORCES": PRINT
540  PRINT "MEMBER"; TAB( 10);"TENS COEFF"; TAB( 25);"FORCE (";F$;")": PRINT

560 FOR I = 1 TO NM
570  PRINT  TAB( 3);I; TAB( 10);P(I); TAB( 25);P(I) * LE(I): NEXT I
580  END
5000 MG = N - 1
5010 DIM CS(N + 1)
5020 FOR IG = 1 TO MG
5030 IF CM(IG,IG) < > 0.0 THEN 5170
5040 FOR NG = IG + 1 TO N
5045 KG = NG
5050 IF CM(NG,IG) < > 0.0 THEN 5090
5060 IF NG < N THEN 5080
5070  PRINT "SINGULAR MATRIX-NO SOLUTION POSSIBLE !"
5080  NEXT NG
5090 FOR PG = IG TO N
5100 CS(PG) = CM(KG,PG)
5110 CM(KG,PG) = CM(IG,PG)
5120 CM(IG,PG) = CS(PG)
5130  NEXT PG
5140 CS(N + 1) = P(KG)
5150 P(KG) = P(IG)
5160 P(IG) = CS(N + 1)
5170 LG = IG + 1
5180 FOR JG = LG TO N
5190 IF CM(JG,IG) = 0.0 THEN 5240
5200 FOR KG = LG TO N
5210 CM(JG,KG) = CM(JG,KG) - CM(IG,KG) * CM(JG,IG) / CM(IG,IG)
```

```
5220  NEXT KG
5230  P(JG) = P(JG) - P(IG) * CM(JG,IG) / CM(IG,IG)
5240  NEXT JG
5250  NEXT IG
5260  P(N) = P(N) / CM(N,N)
5270  FOR IG = 1 TO MG
5280  KG = N - IG
5290  LG = KG + 1
5300  FOR JG = LG TO N
5310  P(KG) = P(KG) - P(JG) * CM(KG,JG)
5320  NEXT JG
5330  P(KG) = P(KG) / CM(KG,KG)
5340  NEXT IG
5350  RETURN
```

Program notes

(1) Lines 5–240   Data input and summary with option to change errors. Note loading is also required at this stage.

(2) Lines 240–490   Build up of tension coefficient equations. A joint number is requested and a check is then made to see if sufficient equations have already been set up (260). As a joint may be restrained, such information is also requested (270, 280) and equations ignored appropriately (360). The number of each member meeting at the joint is required (310, 320), projections (and lengths) calculated (340, 350) and inserted into matrix CM in appropriate locations (370–400). Generally two equations are assembled at each joint but a check is made if only one is required (370). Either one or both of the loading components is inserted in the matrix P(440–460). Zero values of load components are entered at the supports.

(3) Lines 500–590   Solution of equations and print out of results.

Results of the run for this example are shown below. Member numbers are as in the previous example and joint numbers are D = 1, C = 2, E = 3, B = 4, F = 5 and A = 6. F has coordinates (0,0) with x positive to the right and y positive upwards.

```
ANALYSIS OF TRUSS BY METHOD OF
TENSION COEFFICIENTS

NO OF MEMBERS IN TRUSS ?8

NO OF JOINTS (INCLUDING SUPPORTS) ?6

FORCE UNITS,N OR KN ?KN
```

```
X-COORD OF JOINT 1
?2

Y-COORD OF JOINT 1
?0


X-DIRN COMP OF LOADING ?0

Y-DIRN COMP OF LOADING ?-20

X-COORD OF JOINT 2
?2

Y-COORD OF JOINT 2
?1


X-DIRN COMP OF LOADING ?10

Y-DIRN COMP OF LOADING ?0

X-COORD OF JOINT 3
?1

Y-COORD OF JOINT 3
?0


X-DIRN COMP OF LOADING ?0

Y-DIRN COMP OF LOADING ?0

X-COORD OF JOINT 4
?1

Y-COORD OF JOINT 4
 ?1

X-DIRN COMP OF LOADING ?0

Y-DIRN COMP OF LOADING ?0

X-COORD OF JOINT 5
?0

Y-COORD OF JOINT 5
?0


X-DIRN COMP OF LOADING ?0

Y-DIRN COMP OF LOADING ?0

X-COORD OF JOINT 6
?0

Y-COORD OF JOINT 6
?1


X-DIRN COMP OF LOADING ?0

Y-DIRN COMP OF LOADING ?0

POSITIVE END JOINT NO FOR MEMBER 1
?1
```

```
NEGATIVE END JOINT NO FOR MEMBER 1
?3

POSITIVE END JOINT NO FOR MEMBER 2
?2

NEGATIVE END JOINT NO FOR MEMBER 2
?1

POSITIVE END JOINT NO FOR MEMBER 3
?2

NEGATIVE END JOINT NO FOR MEMBER 3
?4

POSITIVE END JOINT NO FOR MEMBER 4
?2

NEGATIVE END JOINT NO FOR MEMBER 4
?3

POSITIVE END JOINT NO FOR MEMBER 5
?3

NEGATIVE END JOINT NO FOR MEMBER 5
?5

POSITIVE END JOINT NO FOR MEMBER 6
?4

NEGATIVE END JOINT NO FOR MEMBER 6
?3

POSITIVE END JOINT NO FOR MEMBER 7
?4

NEGATIVE END JOINT NO FOR MEMBER 7
?6

POSITIVE END JOINT NO FOR MEMBER 8
?4

NEGATIVE END JOINT NO FOR MEMBER 8
?5




DATA SUMMARY

JOINT COORDINATES

JOINT    X-COORD        Y-COORD

  1         2             0
  2         2             1
  3         1             0
  4         1             1
  5         0             0
  6         0             1

PRESS RETURN TO CONTINUE

JOINT LOADING
```

```
JOINT     X=DIRN(KN)       Y-DIRN(KN)

  1         0                -20
  2        10                 0
  3         0                 0
  4         0                 0
  5         0                 0
  6         0                 0
```

PRESS RETURN TO CONTINUE

MEMBER END JOINT NUMBERS

```
MEMBER    +VE END    -VE END

  1         1          3
  2         2          1
  3         2          4
  4         2          3
  5         3          5
  6         4          3
  7         4          6
  8         4          5
```

ANY ERRORS ? TRY AGAIN ? Y/N N

BUILD UP TENSION COEFFICIENT EQUATIONS
JOINT BY JOINT

JOINT NO ?1

IS JOINT RESTRAINED Y/N ?N

NO OF MEMBERS MEETING AT JOINT 1
?2

FIRST MEMBER NO ?1

NEXT MEMBER NO ?2

ANY MORE JOINTS ?Y

JOINT NO ?2

IS JOINT RESTRAINED Y/N ?N

NO OF MEMBERS MEETING AT JOINT 2
?3

FIRST MEMBER NO ?2

NEXT MEMBER NO ?4

NEXT MEMBER NO ?3

ANY MORE JOINTS ?Y

JOINT NO ?3
```
```

```
IS JOINT RESTRAINED Y/N ?N

NO OF MEMBERS MEETING AT JOINT 3
?4

FIRST MEMBER NO ?1

NEXT MEMBER NO ?4

NEXT MEMBER NO ?6

NEXT MEMBER NO ?5

ANY MORE JOINTS ?Y

JOINT NO ?4

IS JOINT RESTRAINED Y/N ?N

NO OF MEMBERS MEETING AT JOINT 4
?4

FIRST MEMBER NO ?7

NEXT MEMBER NO ?8

NEXT MEMBER NO ?6

NEXT MEMBER NO ?3

ANY MORE JOINTS ?N

PROCEEDING TO SOLVE EQUATIONS


MEMBER FORCES

MEMBER    TENS COEFF      FORCE (KN)

   1       0               0
   2       20              20
   3       30              30
   4      -20             -28.2842713
   5      -20             -20
   6       20              20
   7       50              50
   8      -20             -28.2842713
```

PROBLEMS

(4.1) Use the programs to analyse some pin-jointed truss problems of your own or from other sources. Always check the forces for equilibrium; you may find the Method of Sections very useful for this purpose. The reactions at the supports can be checked against adjoining member forces using the program in Example 4.1.

(4.2) Analyse the truss of Figure 4.3 with a variety of different loads or with some joints and members removed (what will happen if the resulting truss is a mechanism?). Observe the resulting forces carefully to gain a feel for the structural behaviour. Carry out further, similar analyses and try to anticipate the forces from your experience. It may be worthwhile to consider Problem (4.3) below before attempting this problem.

(4.3) In order to save repetitive data input for each run, the program given in Example 4.3 could be modified in the following way. After line 240 store NM, NJ, FS, X, Y, PX, PY, EP, EN in the appropriate order, on disc or cassette. When rerunning call up these data before line 20. This will consist of opening files and so on, and will vary from computer to computer. Insert more frequent requests for changes, i.e. after lines 35, 80 and 110, to enable rapid changes of data. Carry out these modifications and do not forget to SAVE the modified version!

(4.4) Using the modified program suggested in Problem (4.3) or otherwise, investigate the effects of changing the joint positions of the truss shown in Figure 4.3. Try to check and understand the output thus building up the experience to predict the likely outcome of a new joint configuration.

Chapter 5

Displacement analysis of trusses

ESSENTIAL THEORY

5.1 Introduction

It has been remarked that in the linear elastic analysis of structures, displacements are assumed to be small. This means that any displacements of the joints of a truss when loaded are not sufficient to significantly alter the equilibrium forces in the members. This also means that the original geometry of the truss and the direction of loading remain unchanged. If a structure does not possess this property either by design or due to overloading, then non-linear theory, beyond the scope of this book must be used in the analysis.

Nevertheless, the smallness of the displacements is relative and the absolute values must be checked firstly to see whether they are excessive for the serviceability of the structure and secondly to check that the above assumptions about the forces are still valid.

Two methods of determining the joint displacement component of a truss are dealt with in this Chapter. The first involves a graphical construction which is only really suitable for statically determinate trusses. The second method uses one of the most powerful principles of mechanics, the *principle of virtual work*, which is applicable to any structure.

5.2 Williot–Mohr diagram

5.2.1 Member elongation

The force induced in a pin-jointed member by the external loading gives rise to (and is also the result of) a change in length of the member e. This is easily calculated from the expression

$$e = \frac{FL}{EA} \tag{5.1}$$

where e has the units mm when F, member force, has units N; E, Young's Modulus for the material, has units N/mm^2; A, the cross-sectional area, has units mm^2 and L, the length of the member, has units mm (or other suitable, consistent units). If F is taken to be positive tensile then e is positive when indicating an extension and negative when indicating a contraction.

Obviously, the displacements of the joints will depend on these member elongations. It is also clear that a joint displacement is not just dependent upon the elongation of those members connected to it. The elongation of every member will have an influence on the joint displacement and the following methods reflect this fact.

5.2.2 The Williot diagram

Consider the simple two bar truss shown in Figure 5.1(a). Joints A and B are fixed to a supporting wall and the displacement of joint C is required due to the applied loading. By resolution it can be shown that the member forces are $F_{BC} = -20\,\text{kN}$ and $F_{AC} = 28.3\,\text{kN}$. With these forces and member properties shown, the elongations calculated from Equation (5.1) are $e_{AC} = 2\,\text{mm}$ (extension) and $e_{BC} = 1\,\text{mm}$ (contraction). These are shown in Figure 5.1(b) in which we imagine we have removed the pin at joint C and allowed each member to elongate without rotating. C on BC moves to C″ and C on AC to C′. We now rotate the members until the free ends C′ and C″ overlap to give the new position C‴ of joint C. This is shown in Figure 5.1(c) in which C′ and C″ describe circular arcs the intersection of which gives the location C‴.

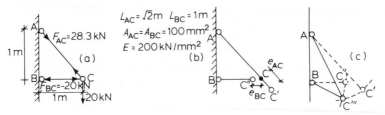

Figure 5.1

If we consider how small the elongations are compared with the member lengths it can be seen that this is not a practical method of construction. One solution would be to greatly exaggerate the elongation so that, in effect, the member lengths shrink to zero and A and B become a single point. This is illustrated in Figure 5.2. Joints A and B are replaced by a single point a,b where joints are given lower case letters on the diagram. The elongation of BC is now represented to a suitable scale by bc″ in the unrotated direction and the length of

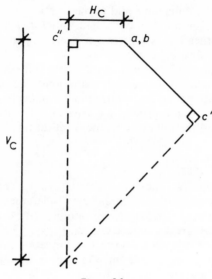

Figure 5.2

BC is ignored. Similarly ac' represents the movement of C on AC. Consider carefully the directions of ac' and bc''. In order to plot the new position of joint C on this diagram we make a further assumption that the exaggerated arcs of rotation in Figure 5.1(c) become straight lines at right angles to the directions of elongation. These construction lines are shown in Figure 5.2 intersecting at c which locates the new position of joint C.

What has been plotted in Figure 5.2 are the *relative* movements of joints. Clearly joints A and B have zero relative movement and form a single point. Joint C has a movement bc'' relative to B in magnitude and direction as shown and a movement of ac' relative to A. The combined effect of these movements is given by the construction lines which intersect at c. The vector ac, with compoments H_C and V_C is clearly now the relative movement of joint C with respect to joint A (or B). As A is a fixed support these components represent the absolute displacement of joint C. This is an example of a Williot diagram.

5.2.3 Williot diagram for a truss

Statically determinate trusses are built up from triangular subframes similar to that considered in the last section. Thus if a further joint D is added to the cantilevered truss of Figure 5.1(a) as shown in

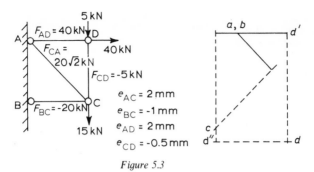

Figure 5.3

Figure 5.3, the Williot diagram of Figure 5.2 may be extended to locate *d*. Both *b* and *c* are already located and the relative movements of joint D with respect to joint B and C are given by the extensions of BD and CD. The right angled construction lines give the location *d*. Once more, the important thing to consider is the direction of the relative movements. Thus for the location of *d″* imagine C is fixed and decide whether D moves upwards or downwards.

More generally, trusses are simply supported rather than cantilevered and it is not possible to find two supports without relative movement. However, one support such as A on the symmetrically loaded truss shown in Figure 5.4(a), must be fixed and this may be used as the starting point for the Williot diagram. To draw the first elongation line, say *ab* for member AB, some assumptions about the rotation of AB must be made. Normally this is taken to be zero and *ab* is drawn in the same direction as AB on the undeformed truss. Thus *ab* is the base line upon which the Williot diagram *abcdefgh* for the truss is constructed and his is shown in Figure 5.4(b). You should check the diagram through, making sure that you understand the directions of the plotted elongations.

5.2.4 Mohr correction diagram

From the Williot diagram in Figure 5.4(b), we can determine the displacement components of each joint relative to the fixed support A. These should be the absolute displacement components but, in particular, joint H has an upward vertical deflection $\delta = 5.3$ mm relative to A which clearly should not happen. This is a result of our assumption that AB does not rotate as illustrated in Figure 5.4(c) in which the new joint locations are plotted from the Williot diagram.

Suppose that we were now able to rotate the truss about A, without straining (rigid body movement), through an anticlockwise angle α so that joint H moved to a new location H′ on the horizontal through H̄

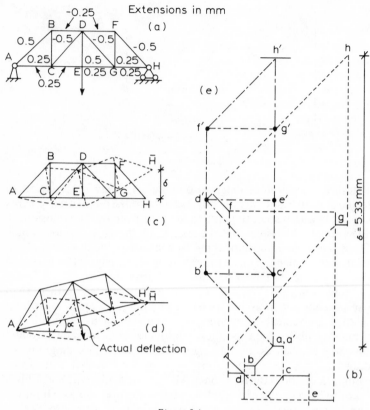

Figure 5.4

as shown in Figure 5.4(d). Measuring the joint locations from these new positions of the joints would give the actual deflections (at least as close as the very small errors involved in the rotation). We could have tried to subtract (vectorially) the spurious deflection of joint H or proportions of it from each joint deflection but the rotation has the same effect and has the advantage that the new rotated position of the joints relative to A can easily be plotted on the Williot diagram.

Firstly, note that during the rigid body rotation, H moves up δ relative to A hence h' is located on the Williot diagram as shown. The small horizontal displacement of H during rotation is ignored but this will only be reasonable for joints lying along the horizontal through A (such as C, E and G). Clearly a joint directly above A would move almost solely horizontally with a small negligible vertical movement. The movements of joints C, E and G relative to A will be proportions of δ and c', e' and g' can thus be located.

The displacements of the other joints due to this rigid body rotation can be found using expressions derived in the Appendix. The locations b', d' and f' are shown in Figure 5.4(e) and the *actual* displacement components of a joint such as D are given in magnitudes and direction by moving *from d' to d* on the Williot diagram as shown.

The displacement diagram for the rigid body rotation $a'b'c'd'e'f'g'h'$ is known as the Mohr correction diagram and the whole diagram is called the Williot–Mohr diagram. It is no coincidence that when the points on the Mohr diagram are connected, the resulting diagram appears to be a scale diagram of the original structure rotated through 90° in the same direction as α; the spurious displacement δ providing the scale. This is true of any shaped structure providing α is small and this fact greatly facilitates the construction of the Mohr diagram.

To draw the Mohr correction diagram we therefore only need to know the true movement of two joints of the structure. Thus H can only move horizontally and h' must therefore lie on the horizontal through h. A is the fixed joint and a' coincides with a. Hence δ can be found and the Mohr construction follows. If H was constrained to run at some angle β to the horizontal then h' would lie on a construction line drawn at β to the horizontal through h. The vertical through A cuts this line at h' giving a new δ and a different Mohr diagram.

Obviously, if we were to choose an actual non-rotating member as our base line for the Williot diagram then no spurious deflections should occur and the Mohr correction diagram shrinks to a point and can be ignored. Such members are often difficult to detect but in the case of the symmetrically loaded truss with symmetrical member properties which we have been investigating, member ED does not rotate. If you start with the assumption that E or D is a fixed joint and ED is non-rotating and hence construct the Williot diagram you will find that a Mohr correction is unnecessary. Although we have assumed, incorrectly, that E or D is fixed, we are plotting relative displacements and providing we locate the true fixed joint A on the diagram, absolute displacements can then be found.

5.3 Virtual work method for joint displacements

5.3.1 Notation

First of all, let us consider some examples of the notation to be used in this section.

F will be used to indicate the force in a member (tension positive). A two letter subscript will indicate the member and single letter superscript will indicate the external load producing the member force. *P*, *Q*, *R*, etc. will be used for external forces and thus,

F_{AB}^P is the force in member AB produced by a load *P*,
F_{BC}^{P+Q} is the force in member BC produced by *P* and load *Q* acting together.

The special superscript 1 will indicate that the force is produced by a unit load (1N or 1 kN as required) applied to the truss at some joint, thus,

F_{AB}^1 is the force in member AB produced by a unit load applied to the truss.

Member elongation will be designated *e* (extension positive) and it follows from above that,

e_{AB}^P is the elongation of member AB produced by load *P*,
e_{BC}^{P+Q} is the elongation of member BC produced by load *P* and load *Q* acting together
e_{FG}^1 is the elongation of member FG produced by a unit load.

Joint displacements will have two components *u* in the *x* or horizontal direction and *v* in the *y* or vertical direction. The sign of these components will not necessarily mean a displacement to the left or right but will indicate direction in a way that will be shown later. Thus,

u_G^P is the horizontal component of the displacement of joint G due to loading P,
v_F^{P+Q} is the vertical component of the displacement of joint F due to loads P and Q acting together.

Providing we are in the elastic range of material behaviour, the principle of superposition ensures that,

$$F_{BC}^{P+Q} = F_{BC}^P + F_{BC}^Q$$
$$e_{BC}^{P+Q} = e_{BC}^P + e_{BC}^Q$$

and $v_F^{P+Q} = v_F^P + v_F^Q$

5.3.2 Work and energy

Work is done by a force when it moves in the direction of its line of action and is the product of the magnitude of the force and the distance moved. Energy is the total work done by a force as it changes position. Energy is frequently the total work done by all the forces within a structure and is a summation (or integral) over the volume as well as the distances travelled by the forces. Energy is dissipated or lost when a force moves in the direction in which it is acting and stored or gained when the opposite occurs.

From the discussion above, when a constant force F moves through a distance d in the direction in which it is acting then it does work equal to Fd and dissipates energy Fd. However, consider what happens to the energy internally and externally, when the truss in Figure 5.5(a) is loaded by a force P as shown. Unless we drop the load on the joint (which is an impact problem not covered here), we must assume that P is applied *gradually* from zero. This application may be fairly fast (the speed at which a weight may be placed and released on a hanger say) but, for a linear elastic truss, the load displacement path will be the striaght line shown in Figure 5.5(b). The force and the

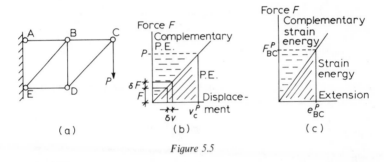

Figure 5.5

displacement vary linearly and the energy dissipated during the loading process is

$$\int_0^{v_C^P} F\,\delta v = \int_0^{v_C^P} \frac{pv}{v_C^P}\,\mathrm{d}v = \frac{1}{2}P\frac{v_C^{P^2}}{v_C^P} = \frac{1}{2}P.v_C^P$$

This energy is lost since the load P clearly moves in the direction of its action. The energy of such loads is known as Potential Energy (PE) and is clearly equal to the shaded area under the load displacement curve. We could have integrated over the force range, the energy being

$$\int_0^P v\,\delta F = \int_0^P \frac{v_C^P}{P}.F\,F = \frac{1}{2}Pv_C^P$$

This is exactly the same as the PE lost but is known as Complementary Potential Energy (CPE). They have the same numerical value and form only when the material is linear elastic.

The force and extension path during loading for a member such as BC is shown in Figure 5.5(c). The energy *stored* will be

$$\int_0^{e_{BC}^P} F \, de = \int_0^{e_{BC}^P} \frac{F_{BC}^P}{e_{BC}^P} . e \, de = \frac{1}{2} F_{BC}^P . e_{BC}^P = U_{BC}$$

This energy is known as the Strain Energy (U) and is stored as a result of the tensile or compressive force in the member moving in a direction opposite to thae action (i.e. in the tensile case, the force pulls on a joint which moves in a direction that extends the member). The Complementary Strain Energy $(\bar{U})$ is illustrated in Figure 5.5(c).

For conservation of energy, the total PE(Π) must equal the total stored Strain Energy, thus

$$\Pi = \frac{1}{2} P v_C^P = \frac{1}{2} F_{AB}^P e_{AB}^P + \frac{1}{2} F_{BC}^P e_{BC}^P + \ldots$$

$$= \sum_{\text{All members}} \frac{1}{2} F^P e^P = U$$

If we consider two vertical loads P and Q applied at C and D *simultaneously*, then

$$\frac{1}{2} P v_C^{P+Q} + \frac{1}{2} Q v_D^{P+Q} = \sum_{\text{All members}} \frac{1}{2} F^{P+Q} e^{P+Q}$$

However, if we apply them separately, then the energy equation is different. We will discuss this later.

5.3.3 Virtual work

Now imagine that the truss has been initially loaded with a unit vertical load (say 1 kN) at joint D. Figure 5.6(a) shows the 'unit load' forces that develop in the members. If the force P is now applied at joint C as before (Figure 5.6(b)), we note the following:

(1) The force in a typical member has increased linearly from F^1 to F^{1+P}

(2) The elongation in each member has increased by that due to the load P, i.e. e^P.

(3) The load P has linearly increased to full value and has moved through a vertical distance v_C^P, just as it did without the initial loading.

(4) The unit load at D remains constant and moves through a distance v_D^P, the vertical deflection at D due to loading P.

Of course, the joints will have had initial displacement due to the unit

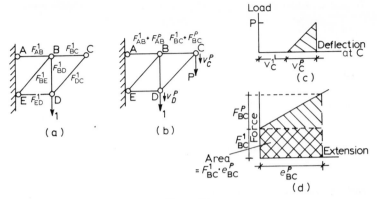

Figure 5.6

load but we will consider only what happens after we apply the load P, when, as we have assumed in the above statements, the extra displacements, forces and extensions are due only to this load.

The loss in potential energy of P and strain energy in a typical member BC when P is applied to the initially loaded structure can be seen in Figure 5.6(c) and (d).

The load P, as before, will have lost potential energy equal to $\frac{1}{2}Pv_C^P$ but the member BC will have gained strain energy equal to $\frac{1}{2}F_{BC}^P e_{BC}^P + F_{BC}^1 \cdot e_{BC}^P$. The extra strain energy is due to the initial force in the member which moves, unchanged, through an elongation e_{BC}^P. In a similar way, Figure 5.7 shows the potential energy lost by the unit load at D. This remains unchanged during a vertical deflection v_D^P and thus loses potential energy equal to $1 \cdot v_D^P$. Thus the energy balance after the loading at P is

$$\Pi = \tfrac{1}{2}Pv_C^P + 1 \cdot v_D^P = \tfrac{1}{2}F_{AB}^P e_{AB}^P + F_{AB}^1 \cdot e_{AB}^1 + \tfrac{1}{2}F_{BC}^P \cdot e_{BC}^P + F_{BC}^1 e_{BC}^1 + \dots$$

$$= \sum_{\text{All members}} \tfrac{1}{2}F^P e^P + \sum_{\text{All members}} F^1 e^P = U'$$

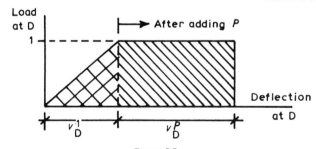

Figure 5.7

Having established that

$$\tfrac{1}{2}Pv_C^P = \sum_{\text{All members}} \tfrac{1}{2}F^P e^P$$

it can be seen that

$$1.v_D^P = \sum_{\text{All members}} F^1 e^P = F_{AB}^1 e_{AB}^P + F_{BC}^1 e_{BC}^P + F_{EB}^1 e_{EB}^P + \dots$$

This is called a *Virtual Work* equation. The reason for the name *Virtual Work* is two-fold. Firstly, the terms are clearly *work* terms involving a force multiplied by a distance moved. Secondly, the displacements and elongations through which the forces move are not (necessarily) developed by those forces. However, we note a fundamental property of the forces and the displacements. The force system F_{AB}^1, F_{BC}^1, etc., and the unit load are in *equilibrium* and the displacement/elongation system v_D^P, e_{AB}^P, e_{BC}^P, ... are *compatible*, that is, the joint displacements result from the elongations without any joints coming apart.

Thus in general, if a system of forces in equilibrium is subjected to any system of displacements and elongations that are compatible then the *internal* virtual work (the sum of the elongations multiplied by member forces) is equal to the *external* virtual work (external loading multiplied by joint displacements) *or* the net virtual work is zero.

The powerful nature of this principle is shown in the above equation where the vertical displacement at joint D due to a load P at joint C is given by the sum of the products of the member elongations due to the load P and the member forces induced by a unit load applied in the direction of the required displacement, i.e. applied vertically at D. For other joint displacements the unit load is applied in the appropriate direction.

The method is easily extended to the case of more than one load when typically,

$$1.v_D^{P+Q} = \sum_{\text{All members}} F^1 . e^{P+Q}$$

An even more powerful property of virtual work is demonstrated in Figure 5.6(d). The virtual work is the rectangular portion of the area under the force displacement curves (straight lines in the figures) and this portion will remain rectangular even if the curves are non-linear (i.e. the material is not linear elastic). Thus equations similar to those above can be used in the solution of non-linear problems.

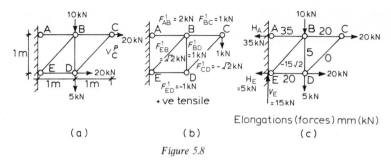

Elongations (forces) mm (kN)

(a)   (b)   (c)

Figure 5.8

5.3.4 Worked example

The truss shown in Figure 5.8(a) is loaded as shown and the vertical displacement of joint C is required. Following the method using the principle of virtual work, a system of forces in equilibrium and a set of compatible elongations and joint displacements are required. The required displacement is v_C (superscript not used; this is assumed to mean that displacement is due to given loading) and to obtain this directly, the external virtual work should be $1.v_C$. Thus a unit load is applied vertically at joint C without any other loading. The member forces due to this load are shown in Figure 5.8(b).

The compatible set of displacements and elongations are the elongations due to the given loading and the joint displacements that result from these. Assuming that $L/EA = 1$ mm/kN for all members then the forces and elongation will be *numerically* equal. Figure 5.8(c) shows these forces and elongations. The external virtual work is the sum of the product of the unit loading and the joint displacements due to the applied loading. Thus,

$$\text{External Virtual Work} = 0.u_C + 1.v_C + 0.u_D + 0.v_D + 0.u_B + 0.v_B$$
$$+ H_A.0 + V_E.0 + H_E.0 = 1.v_C = v_C \text{ kN mm}$$

There is no need to write down each of these terms each time; it is always the case that the external virtual work is numerically equal to the required displacement when we choose only one unit load that acts in the direction of this displacement. However, the expression above shows all the terms concerned and it should be remembered that they do exist. If more than one unit load is applied then the external virtual work will contain two terms; this may not be much use.

The internal virtual work is the sum of the products of the unit load member forces and the member elongations due to the applied loads.

Thus

Internal Virtual Work $= F_{AB}^1 e_{AB} + F_{BC}^1 e_{BC} + \ldots$

$$= (2)(35) + (1)(20) + (-\sqrt{2})(0) + (1)(5)$$
$$+ (-1)(20) + (-\sqrt{2})(-15\sqrt{2})$$
$$= 70 + 20 + 0 + 5 - 20 + 30 = 105 \text{ kN mm}$$

Since the two quantities must be equal,

$$v_C = 105 \text{ mm (downwards)}$$

The positive value for this displacement indicates that it takes place in the direction of the applied unit load. In this case downwards.

WORKED EXAMPLES

Example 5.1 Joint displacements using virtual work

Find the vertical displacement component of joint C of the truss shown in Figure 4.3.

```
5   HOME : PRINT : PRINT "DEFLECTION ANALYSIS OF TRUSS": PRINT : PRINT "BY
        VIRTUAL WORK METHOD": PRINT : PRINT
10  DIM X(20),Y(20),EP(20),EN(20),PX(20),PY(20),LE(20),P(20,2),CM(20,20)
15  DIM EA(20),EX(20),PR(20)
20  PRINT : INPUT "NO OF MEMBERS IN TRUSS ?";NM: PRINT
30  INPUT "NO OF JOINTS (INCLUDING SUPPORTS) ?";NJ: PRINT
35  INPUT "FORCE UNITS,N OR KN ?";F$: PRINT
37  INPUT "LENGTH UNITS,M OR MM ?";L$: PRINT
40  FOR I = 1 TO NJ
50  PRINT "X-COORD OF JOINT ";I: INPUT X(I)
60  PRINT : PRINT "Y-COORD OF JOINT ";I: INPUT Y(I): PRINT
70  PRINT : INPUT "X-DIRN COMP OF LOADING ?";PX(I): PRINT
80  INPUT "Y-DIRN COMP OF LOADING ?";PY(I): PRINT : NEXT I
90  FOR I = 1 TO NM
100 PRINT "POSITIVE END JOINT NO FOR MEMBER ";I: INPUT EP(I): PRINT
110 PRINT "NEGATIVE END JOINT NO FOR MEMBER ";I: INPUT EN(I): PRINT
115 PRINT "CONSISTENT EA VALUE FOR MEMBER ";I: INPUT EA(I): PRINT : NEXT
        I
120 HOME : PRINT : PRINT "DATA SUMMARY": PRINT
130 PRINT "JOINT COORDINATES": PRINT : PRINT "JOINT"; TAB( 10);"X-COORD"
        ; TAB( 25);"Y-COORD": PRINT
140 FOR I = 1 TO NJ: PRINT  TAB( 3);I; TAB( 10);X(I); TAB( 25);Y(I): NEXT
        I
150 PRINT : INPUT,"PRESS RETURN TO CONTINUE";A$
```

```
160   HOME : PRINT : PRINT "JOINT LOADING": PRINT
170   PRINT "JOINT"; TAB( 10);"X=DIRN(";F$;")"; TAB( 25);"Y-DIRN(";F$;")":
      PRINT
180   FOR I = 1 TO NJ: PRINT  TAB( 3);I; TAB( 10);PX(I); TAB( 25);PY(I): NEXT
      I
190   PRINT : INPUT "PRESS RETURN TO CONTINUE";A$
200   HOME : PRINT : PRINT "MEMBER END JOINT NUMBERS": PRINT
210   PRINT "MEMBER"; TAB( 8);"+V E END"; TAB( 17);"-VE END"; TAB( 26);"EA
      VALUE": PRINT
220   FOR I = 1 TO NM: PRINT  TAB( 3);I; TAB( 10);EP(I); TAB( 20);EN(I); TAB(
      26);EA(I): NEXT I
230   PRINT : INPUT "ANY ERRORS ? TRY AGAIN ? Y/N ";A$
240   IF A$ = "Y" THEN 20
250   HOME : PRINT : PRINT "BUILD UP TENSION COEFFICIENT EQUATIONS": PRINT
      "JOINT BY JOINT"
255 R = 0:R1 = 0
260   PRINT : PRINT : INPUT "JOINT NO ?";I:FI = 0:R = R + 1: IF 2 * R - 1 -
      R1 > NM THEN 510
270   PRINT : INPUT "IS JOINT RESTRAINED Y/N ?";A$: PRINT : IF A$ = "N" THEN
      290
280   INPUT "IN X-DIRN (1) OR Y-DIRN (2) ?";FI
290   PRINT : PRINT "NO OF MEMBERS MEETING AT JOINT ";I: INPUT NO
300   FOR II = 1 TO NO: IF II > 1 THEN 320
310   PRINT : INPUT "FIRST MEMBER NO ?";J: GOTO 330
320   PRINT : INPUT "NEXT MEMBER NO ?";J: PRINT
330 K = EP(J):L = EN(J):HP = X(K) - X(L): IF I = K THEN HP =  - HP
340 VP = Y(K) - Y(L): IF I = K THEN VP =  - VP
350 LE(J) =  SQR (HP * HP + VP * VP)
360  IF FI > 0 THEN 390
370 CM(2 * R - 1 - R1,J) = HP: IF 2 * R - 1 - R1 = NM THEN 410
380 CM(2 * R - R1,J) = VP: GOTO 410
390 V = HP: IF FI = 1 THEN V = VP
400 CM(2 * R - 1 - R1,J) = V
410  NEXT II
412 V(1) = 0.0:V(2) = 0.0: PRINT
414  INPUT "DISPLACEMENT REQUIRED AT JOINT ?";A$: IF A$ = "N" THEN 420
416  JN = I: PRINT : INPUT "DISPLACEMENT REQUIRED IN X-DIRN(1) OR Y-DIRN(2
     ) ?";VN
418  V(VN) =  - 1.0
420  IF FI = 0 THEN 460
430  IF FI = 1 THEN 450
440  P(2 * R - R1 - 1,1) =  - PX(I):P(2 * R - R1 - 1,2) = V(1):R1 = R1 + 1
     : GOTO 490
```

```
450 P(2 * R - R1 - 1,1) = - PY(I):P(2 * R - R1 - 1,2) = V(2):R1 = R1 + 1
    : GOTO 490
460 P(2 * R - R1 - 1,1) = - PX(I):P(2 * R - R1 - 1,2) = V(1): IF 2 * R -
    R1 - 1 < NM THEN 480
470 PRINT : PRINT "ENOUGH EQUATIONS-PROCEEDING TO SOLVE": PRINT : GOTO 5
    20
480 P(2 * R - R1,1) = - PY(I):P(2 * R - R1,2) = V(2)
490 PRINT : INPUT "ANY MORE JOINTS ?";A$: IF A$ = "Y" THEN 260
500 PRINT : PRINT "PROCEEDING TO SOLVE EQUATIONS ": PRINT : GOTO 520
510 PRINT : PRINT "NO MORE JOINTS REQUIRED-SOLVING !": PRINT
520 N = NM: GOSUB 5000
530 HOME : PRINT : PRINT "MEMBER FORCES": PRINT
540 PRINT "NO"; TAB( 4);"TENS COEFF"; TAB( 16);"FORCE (";F$;")"; TAB( 28
    );"UNIT LD FCE": PRINT
560 FOR I = 1 TO NM
565 V1 = P(I,1):V1 = ( INT (V1 * 10 ^ 5)) * 10 ^ - 5:V2 = P(I,1) * LE(I)
    :V2 = ( INT (V2 * 10 ^ 5)) * 10 ^ - 5
567 V3 = P(I,2) * LE(I):V3 = ( INT (V3 * 10 ^ 5)) * 10 ^ - 5
570 PRINT I; TAB( 4);V1; TAB( 16);V2; TAB( 28);V3: NEXT I
575 PRINT : INPUT "PRESS RETURN TO CONTINUE";A$
580 DIS = 0.0
590 FOR I = 1 TO NM
600 EX(I) = P(I,1) * LE(I) * LE(I) / EA(I)
610 PR(I) = EX(I) * P(I,2) * LE(I)
615 DIS = DIS + PR(I)
620 NEXT I
630 HOME : PRINT : PRINT "MEMBER EXTENSIONS AND JOINT DISPLACEMENT": PRINT

640 PRINT "NO"; TAB( 5);"EXTENSION"; TAB( 16);"UNIT LD FCE"; TAB( 32);"P
    RODUCT": PRINT
650 FOR I = 1 TO NM
655 V1 = EX(I):V1 = ( INT (V1 * 10 ^ 5)) * 10 ^ - 5:V2 = P(I,2) * LE(I):
    V2 = ( INT (V2 * 10 ^ 5)) * 10 ^ - 5
657 V3 = ( INT (PR(I) * 10 ^ 5)) * 10 ^ - 5
660 PRINT I; TAB( 5);V1; TAB( 16);V2; TAB( 29);V3
670 NEXT I
680 D$ = "X": IF VN = 2 THEN D$ = "Y"
690 PRINT : PRINT "DISPLACEMENT IN ";D$;" DIRECTION": PRINT
700 PRINT "OF JOINT ";JN;" IS ";DIS;L$: PRINT
710 END
5000 MG = N - 1
5010 DIM CS(N + 2)
5020 FOR IG = 1 TO MG
5030 IF CM(IG,IG) < > 0.0 THEN 5170
```

```
5040  FOR NG = IG + 1 TO N
5045  KG = NG
5050  IF CM(NG,IG) < > 0.0 THEN 5090    5100
5060  IF NG < N THEN 5080
5070  PRINT "SINGULAR MATRIX-NO SOLUTION POSSIBLE !"
5080  NEXT NG
5090  FOR PG = IG TO N
5100  CS(PG) = CM(KG,PG)
5110  CM(KG,PG) = CM(IG,PG)
5120  CM(IG,PG) = CS(PG)
5130  NEXT PG
5140  CS(N + 1) = P(KG,1)
5145  CS(N + 2) = P(KG,2)
5150  P(KG,1) = P(IG,1):P(KG,2) = P(IG,2)
5160  P(IG,1) = CS(N + 1)
5165  P(IG,2) = CS(N + 2)
5170  LG = IG + 1
5180  FOR JG = LG TO N
5190  IF CM(JG,IG) = 0.0 THEN 5240
5200  FOR KG = LG TO N
5210  CM(JG,KG) = CM(JG,KG) - CM(IG,KG) * CM(JG,IG) / CM(IG,IG)
5220  NEXT KG
5230  P(JG,1) = P(JG,1) - P(IG,1) * CM(JG,IG) / CM(IG,IG)
5235  P(JG,2) = P(JG,2) - P(IG,2) * CM(JG,IG) / CM(IG,IG)
5240  NEXT JG
5250  NEXT IG
5260  P(N,1) = P(N,1) / CM(N,N)
5265  P(N,2) = P(N,2) / CM(N,N)
5270  FOR IG = 1 TO MG
5280  KG = N - IG
5290  LG = KG + 1
5300  FOR JG = LG TO N
5310  P(KG,1) = P(KG,1) - P(JG,1) * CM(KG,JG)
5315  P(KG,2) = P(KG,2) - P(JG,2) * CM(KG,JG)
5320  NEXT JG
5330  P(KG,1) = P(KG,1) / CM(KG,KG)
5335  P(KG,2) = P(KG,2) / CM(KG,KG)
5340  NEXT IG
5350  RETURN
```

Program notes

(1) This program is essentially the same as that given in Example 4.3
with two exceptions:

(a) The load vector P now has two columns (see Line 10). The first contains the actual loading components (with appropriate sign) and the second contains a unit load (-1, in fact, for loads applied in the positive x and y-directions) in the location corresponding to the required displacement.

(b) The subroutine solving the simultaneous equations (5000–5350) is changed to solve for the two load vectors in one call (see lines 5160–5165, 5230, 5235, 5260, 5265, etc.).

(2) Lines 5–240   Data input, summary and change option.

(3) Lines 250–510   Setting up sufficient tension coefficient equilibrium equations. The same procedure as used in the program given in Example 4.3 with additional input at 414 and 416 of the position and direction of the required displacement. Lines 440–460 show the construction of the two load vectors (note in 412, V(1) and V(2) are set to zero).

(4) Lines 530–575 Printout of forces due to actual and unit loads. 565, 567 and 570 reduce the number of figures printed out for each variable.

(5) Lines 580–710 Virtual work calculated for the required displacement (590–620) and printout of value. This will be positive in the positive x and y-directions chosen.

The truss data used in this example are the same as those used in Example 4.3, i.e. with reference to Figure 4.3, member numbers are DE = 1, CD = 2, BC = 3, CE = 4, EF = 5, BE = 6, AB = 7 and BF = 8; joint numbers are D = 1, C = 2, E = 3, B = 4, F = 5 and A = 6. F is the coordinate origin with x positive to the right and y positive upwards. Only the final part of the output is shown below. EA = 10^5 kN for all member (line 115).

```
DATA SUMMARY

JOINT COORDINATES

JOINT     X-COORD          Y-COORD

  1        2                0
  2        2                1
  3        1                0
  4        1                1
  5        0                0
  6        0                1

PRESS RETURN TO CONTINUE

JOINT LOADING

JOINT     X-DIRN(kN)       Y-DIRN(kN)

  1        0                - 20
```

```
2        10              0
3         0              0
4         0              0
5         0              0
6         0              0
```

PRESS RETURN TO CONTINUE

MEMBER END JOINT NUMBERS

MEMBER +V E END -VE END   EA VALUE

```
1        1        3       100000
2        2        1       100000
3        2        4       100000
4        2        3       100000
5        3        5       100000
6        4        3       100000
7        4        6       100000
8        4        5       100000
```

ANY ERRORS ? TRY AGAIN ? Y/N N

BUILD UP TENSION COEFFICIENT EQUATIONS
JOINT BY JOINT

JOINT NO ?1

IS JOINT RESTRAINED Y/N ?N

NO OF MEMBERS MEETING AT JOINT 1
?2

FIRST MEMBER NO ?1

NEXT MEMBER NO ?2

DISPLACEMENT REQUIRED AT JOINT ?N

ANY MORE JOINTS ?Y

JOINT NO ?2

IS JOINT RESTRAINED Y/N ?N

NO OF MEMBERS MEETING AT JOINT 2
?3

FIRST MEMBER NO ?3

NEXT MEMBER NO ?4

NEXT MEMBER NO ?2

DISPLACEMENT REQUIRED AT JOINT ?Y

DISPLACEMENT REQUIRED IN X-DIRN(1) OR Y-DIRN(2) ?2

ANY MORE JOINTS ?Y

```
JOINT NO ?3

IS JOINT RESTRAINED Y/N ?N


NO OF MEMBERS MEETING AT JOINT 3
?4

FIRST MEMBER NO ?5

NEXT MEMBER NO ?6


NEXT MEMBER NO ?4


NEXT MEMBER NO ?1


DISPLACEMENT REQUIRED AT JOINT ?N

ANY MORE JOINTS ?Y


JOINT NO ?4

IS JOINT RESTRAINED Y/N ?N


NO OF MEMBERS MEETING AT JOINT 4
?4

FIRST MEMBER NO ?7

NEXT MEMBER NO ?8


NEXT MEMBER NO ?6


NEXT MEMBER NO ?3


DISPLACEMENT REQUIRED AT JOINT ?N

ANY MORE JOINTS ?N

PROCEEDING TO SOLVE EQUATIONS


MEMBER FORCES
```

NO	TENS COEFF	FORCE (KN)	UNIT LD FCE
1	0	0	0
2	20	20	0
3	30	30	-1.00001
4	-20.00001	-28.28428	1.41421
5	-20.00001	-20.00001	.999999999
6	20	20	-1.00001
7	50	50	-2.00001
8	-20.00001	-28.28428	1.41421

```
PRESS RETURN TO CONTINUE
```

```
MEMBER EXTENSIONS AND JOINT DISPLACEMENT

NO   EXTENSION   UNIT LD FCE     PRODUCT

1    0           0              0
2    2E-04       0              0
3    3E-04       -1.00001       -3.1E-04
4    -4.1E-04    1.41421        -5.7E-04
5    -2.1E-04    .999999999     -2.1E-04
6    2E-04       -1.00001       -2.1E-04
7    5E-04       -2.00001       -1.01E-03
8    -4.1E-04    1.41421        -5.7E-04

DISPLACEMENT IN Y DIRECTION

OF JOINT 2 IS -2.83137085E-03M


]
```

The negative sign for the deflection component indicates a *downward* movement.

PROBLEMS

(5.1) Draw the Williot–Mohr diagram for the truss shown in Figure 4.3. Firstly use AF as the reference (therefore no Mohr correction required; why?) and then AB. Take $EA = 10^5$ kN for all members. Check that displacement components are the same from each diagram and that the vertical displacement of C corresponds to the 'Virtual Work' value computed in Example 5.1.

(5.2) Starting with Joint 1 (=D) proceed consecutively round the joints 1, 2, 3 and 4 of the truss shown in Figure 4.3 determining the horizontal then vertical deflections using the given program. If required store the data for the truss as indicated in Problem (4.3). For each run record the unit load forces as successive rows of an 8×8 matrix **U**. Check deflection components with those found from the Williot–Mohr diagrams of (5.1).

(5.3) The matrix **U** has some important uses. Consider $\mathbf{U}^T$, each *column* of which gives the member forces due to a unit load acting in turn in the horizontal then vertical positive directions at each successive joint. If this premultiplies the vector $\bar{\mathbf{p}}$ of actual joint loading (in this case $\bar{p}(1) = 0$; $\bar{p}(2) = 20$; $\bar{p}(3) = 10$; $\bar{p}(4) = 0$, etc.), then the resulting vector **f** will contain the member forces due to the actual loading. Thus

$$\mathbf{U}^T\bar{\mathbf{p}} = \mathbf{f}$$

Try this with your recorded matrix **U** and the given loading. Try it with other loading vectors and check the results with the program of

Example 4.3 (or the program given in this chapter). You may already have some results from Problem (4.2).

(5.4) If **f**, see (5.5), is pre-multiplied by a diagonal matrix, **D**, the terms of which are L/EA for each member in numerical order:

$$\mathbf{D} = \begin{bmatrix} L_1/(EA)_1 \dots \dots \dots \dots \dots \dots \\ \vdots \qquad L_2/(EA)_2 \\ \vdots \qquad\qquad\qquad\qquad\diagdown \\ \vdots \qquad\qquad\qquad\qquad\qquad\diagdown \\ \vdots \qquad\qquad\qquad\qquad\qquad\qquad\diagdown \\ \vdots \qquad\qquad\qquad\qquad\qquad\qquad\qquad L_8/(EA)_8 \end{bmatrix} \begin{array}{l} \text{(for this} \\ \text{problem)} \end{array}$$

the resulting vector **e** will contain the extensions of each member under the applied load ($\bar{\mathbf{p}}$). If **e** is premultiplied by **U**, the resulting vector **w** will contain the displacement components of each joint in turn due to the applied loading ($\bar{\mathbf{p}}$). Thus,

$$\mathbf{e} = \mathbf{Df} = \mathbf{DU}^T\bar{\mathbf{p}}$$

and

$$\mathbf{w} = \mathbf{Ue} = \mathbf{UDU}^T\bar{\mathbf{p}} = \mathbf{F}\bar{\mathbf{p}}$$

F is the *flexibility matrix* of the structure and enables *all* the joint displacements (**w**) to be found for *any* load vector $\bar{\mathbf{p}}$. Find $\mathbf{F} = \mathbf{UDU}^T$ from your recorded values and check as many load cases as you can.
(5.5) Modify the given program to calculate and print out the flexibility matrix for a given truss. Firstly, no loading input is required (lines 70 and 80). **P** is now an $NM \times NM$ diagonal matrix containing -1.0 in each diagonal term (thus 414–460 is probably not required). The equation solving subroutine must be altered to deal with NM columns of P (5160, 5165, 5230, 5235, 5260, 5265, etc. replaced by FOR loops). Do not forget that **P** is returned from this subroutine with the tension coefficients, not the forces.

Chapter 6

Deflection of beams – Shear force and bending moment diagram

ESSENTIAL THEORY

6.1 Introduction

Although the displacement of a structure under load is assumed to be small thus enabling us to use the simplified linear theory, it may still have a considerable effect on the serviceability of the structure. Significantly visible deflections may affect public confidence and increase fatigue of the structural components. Deflection may seriously affect cladding or surfaces thus decreasing the useful life of the structure. Thus it is important to develop analytical methods for determining structural deflections and deformations.

Methods for calculating the vertical deflection and slope of the deflection curve of simple beams are developed in this chapter. A brief account of Bending Moment and Shear Force is given and you are referred to reference [2], Section 2.6 for a full discussion.

6.2 Bending moment and shear force

If a vertical section is cut through a loaded beam as shown in Figure 6.1(a) then it is clear that if collapse is to be avoided, forces in equilibrium with those acting on either portion of the beam must be applied to both sides of the cut. Furthermore, the two sets of forces must be equal and opposite so that when the cut is closed no net force is developed. These equal and opposite forces must be present internally at each section of the beam and are developed by (and cause!) the deformation of the beam.

If we imagine the beam to be made of a large number of longitudinal fibres each carrying a force, then the distribution of these forces across the cut section may be complex. However, they can be resolved and summed to give three overall components,

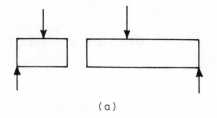

(a)

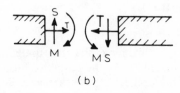

(b)

Figure 6.1

Shear Force S
Bending Moment M
Axial Force T

These components form equal and opposite pairs at a section.

The bending moment, shear force and axial force at any section can be found by considering equilibrium of the 'cut-off' portion of the beam to the left or right of the section. This is three equations of equilibrium in three unknown components. Note that the beam is not *actually* cut but this is a simple device for visualising the force system at a section. The direction of action of M, S and T is distinguished by using a sign convention. These are purely arbitrary and will vary from text to text and person to person. The positive directions used in this work are shown in Figure 6.1(b).

Thus we do not need to know anything about the distribution of the fibre forces (or, if each fibre has unit area, the stresses) to determine their resultants M, S and T. In fact we may use the values of M, S and T to find the section stresses (see reference [2], Section 2.6).

6.3 Bending moment and shear force diagrams

A Bending Moment Diagram (BMD) or Shear Force Diagram (SFD) is a plot of M or S at each section of the beam drawn to a suitable scale along a base line representing the beam. These values are calculated from the Free Body Diagram (the beam with supports replaced by the

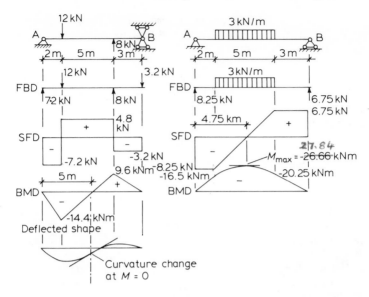

Figure 6.2

actual reactive forces) by considering equilibrium of fictitious 'cut' portions of the beam. Each diagram should clearly show its shape, maximum values with units, signs and positions of maximum and zero values.

Figure 6.2 shows two examples of the construction of these diagrams for a simply supported beam. It is worth working through these to make sure you understand the method of calculating moments and shear forces and determining the signs. In particular there are several useful facts which can be checked:

(a) Shear force is equal to the rate of change of bending moment i.e. $S = dM/dx$. Thus the slope of the M diagram at any point is equal to the shear force at that point. More important, *maximum* or *minimum* values of the bending moment are located where the shear force is *zero*.

(b) In the absence of any other loading, the bending moment diagram is linear between point loads. Since, at a point load, there is an abrupt change in the shear force then from (a) above, there must be an abrupt change in the slope of the bending moment diagram.

(c) The rate of change of shear force along the beam is equal to the intensity of the uniformly distributed load.

(d) The moment of a length, l, of uniformly distributed load, intensity

q, about any point is equal to the total load along its length, lq, multiplied by the distance from the point to the centre of length of the uniformly distributed load.

Although straightforward and unambiguous for horizontal beams, sign conventions, particularly for bending moments are confusing for columns and bent members. Generally, bending moment diagrams are drawn on the tensile side of such members thus eliminating confusion.

6.4 Bending moment–curvature relationship. The differential equation for vertical deflection

Although the vertical deflection curve of a beam is only truly circular when the beam is subjected to pure bending ($S = 0$), the assumption is made that under any loading conditions, an infinitesimally small portion of the curve may be considered to be a circular arc with radius R which, of course, varies along the beam. The *curvature* at any point is $1/R$ which can be seen to be a measure of the bend in the curve.

There is obviously some relationship between the bending moment applied to the beam at any section and the resulting curvature. To establish this, a further assumption, that originally plane sections remain plane after bending, is made. For most practical beams, this is a reasonable assumption and even where this is not strictly true, the theory developed here gives good results. Thus in Figure 6.3(a), an infinitesimal length of beam Δx is subjected to a bending moment M and the two originally vertical sections $X–X$ and $Y–Y$ remain plane after bending. If these sections are projected, they intersect at 0, the centre of curvature. The radius of curvature extends to the neutral plane on which (in the absence of any axial forces) there is zero stress or strain. This is the origin of the z-axis.

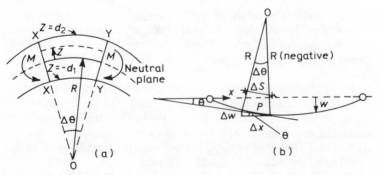

Figure 6.3

It is clear from Figure 6.3(a) that the strain (ε) in each fibre is linearly depdent on z such that:

$$\varepsilon = \frac{(R+z)\Delta\theta - R\Delta\theta}{R\Delta\theta} = \frac{z}{R} \text{ tensive positive}$$

For no axial force and stress $\sigma = E\varepsilon$

$$\int_{-d_1}^{d_2} b\sigma\,dz = \int_{-d_1}^{d_2} bE\frac{z}{R}\,dz = \frac{E}{R}\int_{-d_1}^{d_2} bz\,dz = 0$$

where b is the width of the cross-section at any depth.

Thus $\int_{-d_1}^{d_2} bz\,dz = 0$ and this can only be true if the horizontal neutral plane passes through the centroid of the cross-section of the beam forming the Neutral Axis of the section.

Further,

$$M = \int_{-d_1}^{d_2} b\sigma z\,dz = \frac{E}{R}\int_{-d_1}^{d_2} bz^2\,dz = \frac{E}{R}I_{\text{NA}}$$

where I_{NA} is the second moment of area of the cross-section about the Neutral Axis (see reference [2], Section 2.6 for details of determining second moments of area). Thus, curvature and bending moment are related by,

$$\frac{1}{R} = \frac{M}{EI_{\text{NA}}}$$

Figure 6.3(b) shows an exaggerated deflection curve for a beam. Normally, deflection, w, is measured positive downwards as shown whilst R is positive when the centre of curvature is below the beam as in Figure 6.3(a). The tangent to the curve at a point p makes an angle θ to the x-axis and a small element of beam length Δx subtends and angle $\Delta\theta$ at the centre of curvature. Thus, if Δs is the length of the small element of the deflection curve,

$$R.\Delta\theta = \Delta s \quad \text{and} \quad \frac{1}{R} = \frac{\Delta\theta}{\Delta s}$$

We note that the signs are taken care of here since θ *decreases* as s increases. For small deflections, $\Delta s \doteqdot \Delta x$ and in the limit,

$$\frac{1}{R} = \frac{\Delta\theta}{\Delta x} = \frac{d\theta}{dx} = \frac{d(\tan^{-1} dw/dx)}{dx} = \frac{d^2w/dx^2}{\sqrt{1-(dw/dx)^2}}$$

and for $dw/dx \ll 1$ (a reasonable assumption for small deflection),

$$\frac{1}{R} = \frac{M}{EI_{NA}} = \frac{d^2w}{dx^2}$$

This is the differential equation for beam deflection. Of course, the bending moment M must be known, if not other equations are

$$\frac{d^3w}{dx^3} = \frac{S}{EI_{NA}} \quad \text{and} \quad \frac{d^4w}{dx^4} = \frac{q}{EI_{NA}}$$

where q is the applied (uniformly) distributed load. We will concentrate on the solution of the first equation.

6.5 Solution of differential equation for deflection

6.5.1 Macaulay's double integration method

If general expressions for M in terms of x are known then an expression for the deflection w along the beam can be found simply by integrating the equation twice. Two constants of integration are obtained which can be found from the deflection conditions at the supports (usually zero deflection or slope dw/dx). A quick glance at a typical bending moment diagram will show that, particularly, with point loads, different expressions for M are encountered along the beam. It would seem, therefore, that the double integration processes must be carried out for each of these expressions with the constants of integration determined from slope and deflection continuity at each load. This is a tedious and often impracticable process; for six point loads, fourteen constants must be found!

Macaulay devised a simple method for writing down a single expression for the bending moment along a beam thus requiring the evaluation of only two constants. So-called 'Macaulay terms' are used which are taken to be zero if they evaluate negative. Thus for the beam shown in Figure 6.4(a), the bending moment at any section x is

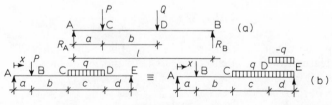

Figure 6.4

$$M = -R_A[x] + P[x-a] + Q[x-b-a] - R_B[x-l]$$

the brackets thus [ ] being Macaulay terms, which are taken as zero if the expression within the brackets is negative.

The origin for x does not have to be at the left-hand side. If it was transferred to C in Figure 6.4(a) then,

$$M = -R_A[x+a] + P[x] + Q[x-b] - R_B[x-(l-a)]$$

A similar set of brackets can be developed for uniformly distributed loads. Thus for a point between C and D on the beam in Figure 6.4(b),

$$M = -R_A[x] + P[x-a] + q/2[x-(a+b)]^2 + \ldots$$

Beyond D, it would appear that Macaulay terms are complicated. However, the simple superposition device shown in the figure permits the u.d.l q to continue to the end of the beam with an equal and opposite u.d.l $-q$ added after D. Thus, for any point along the beam,

$$M = -R_A[x] + P[x-a] + q/2[x-(a+b)]^2 - q/2[x-(a+b+c)]^2$$
$$\div R_E[x-l]$$

where $l = a+b+c+d$.

The differential equation for deflection of the beam in Figure 6.4(a) is now,

$$\frac{d^2w}{dx^2} = \frac{1}{EI_{NA}}\{-R_A[x] + P[x-a] + Q[x-(a+b)] - R_B[x-l]\}$$

With EI_{NA} constant, this may be integrated twice with the Macaulay terms treated as normal brackets for the purposes of this integration,

$$\frac{dw}{dx} = \frac{1}{EI_{NA}}\left\{\frac{-R_A[x]^2}{2} + \frac{P[x-a]^2}{2} + \frac{Q[x-(a+b)]^2}{2} - \frac{R_B[x-l]^2}{2}\right\} + C$$

$$w = \frac{1}{EI_{NA}}\left\{\frac{-R_A[x]^3}{6} + \frac{P[x-a]^3}{6} + \frac{Q[x-(a+b)]^3}{6} - \frac{R_B[x-l]^3}{6}\right\}$$

$$+ Cx + D$$

Where C and D are constants of integration. It is vital that no attempt is made to expand the Macaulay terms at any stage; they would lose their meaning if this was done.

The constants C and D can be found from any two conditions on the deflection w or the slope dw/dx. When substituting values of x for this purpose or when calculating the deflection when C and D have been found, the rules for the Macaulay terms must be observed.

6.5.2 Area moment theorems

Consider again, the governing equation

$$\frac{d^2w}{dx^2} = \frac{M}{EI_{NA}}$$

Integrating this equation between two points X and Y on the beam gives,

$$\int_{x_X}^{x_Y} \frac{d^2w}{dx^2}\,dx = \left[\frac{dw}{dx}\right]_{x_X}^{x_Y} = \theta_Y - \theta_X = \int_{x_X}^{x_Y} \frac{M}{EI_{NA}}\,dx$$

The difference between the slope of the deflection curve between any two points on the beam is equal to the area under the 'M/EI' (or curvature) diagram between the two points. This geometric interpretation of the equation is frequently used as a statement of the *first* Area–Moment Theorem.

Consider now

$$\int_{x_X}^{x_Y} \frac{d^2w}{dx^2}\,dx = \int_{x_X}^{x_Y} x\,d\!\left(\frac{dw}{dx}\right) = \left[x\frac{dw}{dx}\right]_{x_X}^{x_Y} - \int_{x_X}^{x_Y} \frac{dw}{dx}\,dx = [x\theta]_{x_X}^{x_Y} - [w]_{x_X}^{x_Y}$$

Thus

$$[x\theta - w]_{x_X}^{x_Y} = \int_{x_X}^{x_Y} \frac{M}{EI_{NA}}\,x\,dx$$

The left-hand side of this equation is in fact the vertical distance between the slope at X extended and the deflection curve at Y. This is not particularly helpful and it is more useful to consider it as shown. The right-hand side is the moment of the 'M/EI' (or curvature) diagram between X and Y about the origin of x. This is a statement of the *second* Area–Moment Theorem.

It is the geometric interpretation of the integrals which makes this method very useful for hand calculations. The 'M/EI' or curvature diagram is usually composed of triangles, rectangles, trapeziums and areas with parabolic boundaries. Moments and areas are therefore easily computed.

By successive use of these theorems and wise choice of the origin of x, values of θ and w at any section of the beam can be found. There is a strong element of human judgement in the successful use of this method and it does not therefore lend itself readily to computer application.

6.5.3 Virtual work methods

A similar virtual work method to that used in plane trusses (see Section 5.3) can be used to find the deflection or slope at a point along a beam. A unit load or moment is applied at the appropriate location and by equating the 'external' virtual work of the unit load or moment when undergoing the actual deflection or slope to the 'internal' virtual work of the resulting unit load moments and forces when subjected to the actual slopes and deflections, the required quantity is obtained.

We shall restrict our discussion to deflection curves caused purely by bending action. Shear effects tend to complicate the calculations and are known to give only a small contribution to the deflection of thin beams. If it is assumed that the bending moments developed along a loaded beam are subjected to the resulting deflection curve, the work done can be shown to be

$$\int_{\text{Beam Length } L} (\text{moment } M) \times (\text{curvature } k)\, dL$$

Note that even if k results from the same loading as M, this is a 'virtual' work quantity since M remains unchanged during flexure. However, M and k need not be related in any way. Consider the section AB of beam shown in Figure 6.5. This may be loaded with a uniformly distributed load q^*, point loads, P_1^*, P_2^*, etc., and shears and moments S_A^*, S_B^*, M_A^* and M_B^* (Figure 6.5(a)) and be subjected to unrelated deflections w, w_A, w_B and end rotations θ_A and θ_B (Figure 6.5(b)). The virtual work equation is

$$\int_A^B M^* k\, dx = \int_A^B q^* w\, dx + P_1^* w_1 + P_2^* w_2 - M_A^* \theta_A + S_A^* w_A + M_B^* \theta_B - S_B^* w_B$$

$$\underset{\text{v.w.}}{\text{Internal}} \qquad \underset{\text{v.w.}}{\text{External}}$$

Note that θ is the slope of the deflection curve with a positive value when anticlockwise.

This equation could be deduced in a similar way to that for the

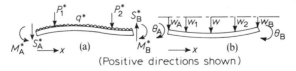

(Positive directions shown)

Figure 6.5

truss. The loading which produced M^*, S^*, etc. is applied first followed by the loading to produce w, w_A, etc.; the virtual work being the respective rectangular areas under the load displacement, moment–curvature graphs (see Section 5.3.3).

In order to find the deflection or slope at some point along the beam, a suitable choice of loading P^*, q^*, etc. and the positions of A and B must be made. Thus, if the deflection w_1 due to some given loading on a simply supported beam is required, then by setting $P_1^* = 1$ (i.e. a downward acting unit load), $q^* = 0$, $p_2^* = 0$,

$$\int_A^B M^* k \, dx = 1.w_1 - M_A^* \theta_A + S_A^* w_A + M_B^* \theta_B - S_B^* w_B$$

As the beam is simply–supported then by choosing A and B to be the ends of the beam, $M_A^* = M_B^* = 0$, $w_A = w_B = 0$

$$\int_A^B M^* k \, dx = 1.w_1$$

k and w_1 are part of the same compatible displacement set due to the actual applied loading. If this loading gives rise to bending moments M along the beam then since $k = M/EI$,

$$1.w_1 = \int_{x=0}^{x=\text{span}} \frac{M^* M}{EI_{NA}} \, dx$$

where M^* is the bending moment due to the unit load $P_1^* = 1$.

Thus functions of x representing the bending moment M due to the actual applied load and M^* due to the unit load (or moment if a slope is required) are multiplied and integrated to give the deflection (or slope) in the direction of the applied unit load (or moment). Frequently the terms involving end moments and shears are ignored and certainly A and B should be chosen so that they are zero. A check should always be made to be sure that the integration limits have been chosen to satisfy this condition.

WORKED EXAMPLES

Example 6.1 Bending moment and shear force

Find the bending moment and shear force at various sections along the simply supported beam shown in Figure 6.2. Consider either or both systems of loading.

```
10   REM  PROGRAM TO DETERMINE BENDING MOMENT AND SHEAR FORCE FOR SIMPLY S
     UPPORTEDBEAM
20   DIM BM(100),SH(100),D(100)
30   HOME
40   PRINT
50   PRINT "BENDING MOMENTS AND SHEAR FORCES DETERMINED FOR SIMPLY SUPPORT
     ED BEAM CARRYING VERTICAL LOADS"
60   PRINT
70   INPUT "LENGTH UNITS ?";L$
80   PRINT
90   INPUT "FORCE UNITS ?";F$
100  PRINT
110  INPUT "SPAN OF BEAM ?";SP
120  PRINT
130  INPUT "POSITION OF L.H. SUPPORT FROM L.H. END ?";XR(1)
140  PRINT
150  INPUT "POSITION OF R.H. SUPPORT FROM L.H. END ?";XR(2)
160  PRINT
170  INPUT "NUMBER OF POINT LOADS ?";NP
180  PRINT
190  INPUT "NUMBER OF UNIFORMLY DISTRIBUTED LOADS ?";NU
200  PRINT
210  IF NP = 0 THEN 300
220  FOR I = 1 TO NP
230  PRINT "FOR POINT LOAD NUMBER ";I;" GIVE
240  PRINT
250  INPUT "MAGNITUDE ";PL(I)
260  PRINT
270  INPUT "DISTANCE FROM LEFT HAND END ";XP(I)
280  PRINT
290  NEXT I
300  IF NU = 0 THEN 410
310  FOR I = 1 TO NU
320  PRINT "FOR U.D.L. NUMBER ";I;" GIVE"
330  PRINT
340  INPUT "INTENSITY ";UL(I)
350  PRINT
360  INPUT "LENGTH ";LU(I)
370  PRINT
380  INPUT "DISTANCE OF START OF LOAD FROM L.H. END ";XU(I)
390  PRINT
400  NEXT I
410  HOME
420  PRINT "DATA SUMMARY"
430  PRINT
440  PRINT "SPAN OF BEAM = ";SP;L$
450  PRINT
```

A : BENDSHEAR

```
460 PRINT "L.H. SUPPORT ";XR(1);L$;" FROM L.H.END"
470 PRINT
480 PRINT "R.H. SUPPORT ";XR(2);L$;" FROM L.H. END"
490 PRINT
500 IF NP = 0 THEN 550
510 PRINT "POINT LOADS": PRINT
520 FOR I = 1 TO NP
530 PRINT PL(I);F$;" AT ";XP(I);L$;" FROM L.H. END ": PRINT
540 NEXT I
545 PRINT : INPUT "PRESS RETURN TO CONTINUE";A$
550 IF NU = 0 THEN 610
560 PRINT "UNIFORMLY DISTRIBUTED LOADS ": PRINT
570 FOR I = 1 TO NU
580 PRINT UL(I);F$;" PER ";L$;",LENGTH ";LU(I);F$
590 PRINT "STARTING ";XU(I);L$;" FROM L.H. END": PRINT
600 NEXT I
610 INPUT "DO YOU WISH TO CHANGE ANYTHING ?";A$: PRINT
620 IF A$ = "Y" THEN 30
630 PRINT "REACTIONS"
640 MSUM = 0:PSUM = 0
650 FOR I = 1 TO NP
660 PSUM = PSUM + PL(I)
670 MSUM = MSUM + PL(I) * XP(I)
680 NEXT I
690 FOR I = 1 TO NU
700 PSUM = PSUM + UL(I) * LU(I)
710 MSUM = MSUM + UL(I) * LU(I) * (XU(I) + LU(I) / 2)
720 NEXT I
730 R(1) = (MSUM / XR(2) - PSUM) / (XR(1) / XR(2) - 1)
740 R(2) = PSUM - R(1)
750 PRINT : PRINT "LH REACTION = ";R(1);F$;" AT ";XR(1);L$;" FROM L.H.EN
    D ": PRINT
760 PRINT "RH REACTION = ";R(2);F$;" AT ";XR(2);L$;" FROM L.H. END ": PRINT

770 REM   760-960   REORDERING OF LOADS INTO DISTANCE ORDER IF REQUIRED
775 IF NP < 2 THEN 865
780 FOR II = 1 TO NP:TE = XP(II):TP = PL(II)
790 K = II
795 IF II = NP THEN 865
800 FOR JJ = II + 1 TO NP
810 IF XP(JJ) > = TE THEN 840
820 K = JJ
830 TE = XP(JJ):TP = PL(JJ)
840 NEXT JJ
850 XP(K) = XP(II):XP(II) = TE:PL(K) = PL(II):PL(II) = TP
```

```
860   NEXT II
865   IF NU = 1 THEN 970
870   FOR II = 1 TO NU
880   TE = XU(II):TP = UL(II):TL = LU(II)
890   K = II
895   IF II = NU THEN 970
900   FOR JJ = II + 1 TO NU
910   IF XU(JJ) > = TE THEN 940
920   K = JJ
930   TE = XU(JJ):TP = UL(JJ):TL = LU(JJ)
940   NEXT JJ
950   XU(K) = XU(II):XU(II) = TE:UL(K) = UL(II):UL(II) = TP:LU(K) = LU(II):
      LU(II) = TL
960   NEXT II
970   PRINT : PRINT : PRINT
980   INPUT "BENDING MOMENT AND SHEAR FORCE REQUIRED AT A SINGLE SECTION ?
      ";A$: PRINT
990   IF A$ = "N" THEN 1090
1000  INPUT "DISTANCE OF SECTION FROM L.H. END ?";XB
1010  GOSUB 2000
1020  PRINT : PRINT "BENDING MOMENT AT ";XB;L$;" FROM L.H. END": PRINT
1030  PRINT MO;F$;L$
1040  PRINT : PRINT "SHEAR FORCE AT ";XB;L$;" FROM L.H. END": PRINT
1050  PRINT SF;F$: PRINT
1060  INPUT "ANY MORE SECTIONS ?";A$: PRINT
1070  IF A$ = "Y" THEN 1000
1080  GOTO 1240
1090  INPUT "INTERVAL AT WHICH BM AND SF ARE REQUIRED ?";XI: PRINT
1100  XB = - XI:II = - 1
1110  XB = XB + XI:II = II + 1
1120  IF XB > SP THEN XB = SP
1130  GOSUB 2000
1140  D(II) = XB:BM(II) = MO:SH(II) = SF
1150  IF XB = SP THEN 1170
1160  GOTO 1110
1170  PRINT "DISTRIBUTION OF BM AND SF ALONG BEAM": PRINT
1180  PRINT "DISTANCE "; TAB( 14);"BENDING MOMENT"; TAB( 30);"SH.FORCE"
1190  PRINT "FROM LH END "
1195  CO = 8
1200  FOR I = 0 TO II
1210  PRINT D(I); TAB( 16);BM(I); TAB( 30);SH(I)
1220  PRINT
1222  IF I < = CO THEN 1230
1224  PRINT : INPUT "PRESS RETURN TO CONTINUE";A$
1226  CO = CO + 8
1230  NEXT I
```

```
1240   END
2000   REM  SUBROUTINE FOR BM AND SF AT XB
2010   MO = 0.0:SF = 0.0
2020   IF XB < = XR(1) THEN 2060
2030   MO = MO + R(1) * (XB - XR(1)):SF = SF + R(1)
2040   IF XB < = XR(2) THEN 2060
2050   MO = MO + R(2) * (XB - XR(2)):SF = SF + R(2)
2060   IF NP = 0 THEN 2110
2070   FOR I = 1 TO NP
2080   IF XB < = XP(I) THEN 2110
2090   MO = MO - PL(I) * (XB - XP(I)):SF = SF - PL(I)
2100   NEXT I
2110   IF NU = 0 THEN 2180
2120   FOR I = 1 TO NU
2130   IF XB < = XU(I) THEN 2180
2140   IF XB < XU(I) + LU(I) THEN 2160
2150   MO = MO - UL(I) * LU(I) * (XB - XU(I) - 0.5 * LU(I)):SF = SF - UL(I)
         * LU(I): GOTO 2170
2160   MO = MO - 0.5 * UL(I) * (XB - XU(I)) * (XB - XU(I)):SF = SF - UL(I) *
         (XB - XU(I))
2165   SF = - SF
2170   NEXT I
2175   REM  SIGN CHANGE FOR SIGN CONVENTION
2180   MO = - MO:SF = - SF
2190   RETURN
```

Program notes

(1) Lines 10–620 The program is interactive and fairly self explanatory. In this section data are input and summarized with an opportunity for changes (610). The length units and force units (70 and 80) are left to the user.

(2) Lines 630–760 Calculation and printout of reactions. Note, supports need not be at the ends of the beam.

(3) Lines 760–960 Loading is ordered by increasing distance from left-hand end. This facilitates the calculation of BMs and SFs.

(4) Lines 980–1080 Calculation of BM and SF at selected sections along the beam.

(5) Lines 1090–1230 Calculation of BM and SF at equally spaced intervals along the beam.

The printout below shows values at selected sections due to the point loading.

BENDING MOMENTS AND SHEAR FORCES DETERMINED FOR SIMPLY SUPPORTED BEAM CARRYING V
ERTICAL LOADS

LENGTH UNITS ?M

FORCE UNITS ?KN

SPAN OF BEAM ?10

POSITION OF L.H. SUPPORT FROM L.H. END ?0

POSITION OF R.H. SUPPORT FROM L.H. END ?10

NUMBER OF POINT LOADS ?2

NUMBER OF UNIFORMLY DISTRIBUTED LOADS ?0

FOR POINT LOAD NUMBER 1 GIVE

MAGNITUDE -8

DISTANCE FROM LEFT HAND END 7

FOR POINT LOAD NUMBER 2 GIVE

MAGNITUDE 12

DISTANCE FROM LEFT HAND END 2

DATA SUMMARY

SPAN OF BEAM = 10M

L.H. SUPPORT 0M FROM L.H.END

R.H. SUPPORT 10M FROM L.H. END

POINT LOADS

-8KN AT 7M FROM L.H. END

12KN AT 2M FROM L.H. END

PRESS RETURN TO CONTINUE
DO YOU WISH TO CHANGE ANYTHING ?N

REACTIONS

LH REACTION = 7.2KN AT 0M FROM L.H.END

RH REACTION = -3.2KN AT 10M FROM L.H. END

BENDING MOMENT AND SHEAR FORCE REQUIRED AT A SINGLE SECTION ?Y

DISTANCE OF SECTION FROM L.H. END ?2

BENDING MOMENT AT 2M FROM L.H. END

-14.4KNM

SHEAR FORCE AT 2M FROM L.H. END

-7.2KN

ANY MORE SECTIONS ?Y

DISTANCE OF SECTION FROM L.H. END ?2.01

BENDING MOMENT AT 2.01M FROM L.H. END

-14.352KNM

SHEAR FORCE AT 2.01M FROM L.H. END

4.8KN

ANY MORE SECTIONS ?N

Note that *loads* are positive *downwards* and *reactions* positive upwards.

Use the program to evaluate BM and SF at equal intervals along the beam for both the point load and uniformly distributed load cases shown in Figure 6.2.

Example 6.2 Vertical deflection: Macaulay's method

Use Macaulay's double integration method to find the vertical deflection at the centre of the span of the simply supported beam shown in Figure 6.2. Take $EI = 10^5$ kNm^2.

```
10   REM  PROGRAM TO CALCULATE VERTICAL DEFLECTION OF A SIMPLY SUPPORTED B
     EAM AT AGIVEN SECTION USING MACAULAYS METHOD
20   DIM XP(30),PL(30),UL(30),LU(30),XU(30)
30   HOME
40   PRINT
50   PRINT "VERTICAL DEFLECTION OF A SIMPLY SUPPORTED BEAM BY MACAULAYS ME
     THOD "
60   PRINT
70   INPUT "LENGTH UNITS,M OR MM ?";L$
80   PRINT
90   INPUT "FORCE UNITS,N OR KN ?";F$
100   PRINT
104   INPUT "DEFLECTION UNITS,M OR MM ?";W$
105   PRINT
110   INPUT "SPAN OF BEAM ?";SP
120   PRINT
130   INPUT "POSITION OF L.H. SUPPORT FROM L.H. END ?";XR(1)
140   PRINT
150   INPUT "POSITION OF R.H. SUPPORT FROM L.H. END ?";XR(2)
160   PRINT
164   INPUT "CONSISTENT EI VALUE ?";EI
166   PRINT
168   PRINT "INPUT LOAD DATA IN ANY ORDER": PRINT
170   INPUT "NUMBER OF POINT LOADS ?";NP
180   PRINT
190   INPUT "NUMBER OF UNIFORMLY DISTRIBUTED LOADS ?";NU
200   PRINT
210   IF NP = 0 THEN 300
220   FOR I = 1 TO NP
230   PRINT "FOR POINT LOAD NUMBER ";I;" GIVE
240   PRINT
250   INPUT "MAGNITUDE ";PL(I)
260   PRINT
```

```
270  INPUT "DISTANCE FROM LEFT HAND END ";XP(I)
280  PRINT
290  NEXT I
300  IF NU = 0 THEN 410
310  FOR I = 1 TO NU
320  PRINT "FOR U.D.L. NUMBER ";I;" GIVE"
330  PRINT
340  INPUT "INTENSITY ";UL(I)
350  PRINT
360  INPUT "LENGTH ";LU(I)
370  PRINT
380  INPUT "DISTANCE OF START OF LOAD FROM L.H. END ";XU(I)
390  PRINT
400  NEXT I
410  HOME
420  PRINT "DATA SUMMARY"
430  PRINT
440  PRINT "SPAN OF BEAM = ";SP;L$
450  PRINT
454  PRINT "EI = ";EI;F$;L$;"^2"
456  PRINT
460  PRINT "L.H. SUPPORT ";XR(1);L$;" FROM L.H.END"
470  PRINT
480  PRINT "R.H. SUPPORT ";XR(2);L$;" FROM L.H. END"
490  PRINT
500  IF NP = 0 THEN 550
510  PRINT "POINT LOADS": PRINT
520  FOR I = 1 TO NP
530  PRINT PL(I);F$;" AT ";XP(I);L$;" FROM L.H. END ": PRINT
540  NEXT I
550  IF NU = 0 THEN 610
560  PRINT "UNIFORMLY DISTRIBUTED LOADS ": PRINT
570  FOR I = 1 TO NU
580  PRINT UL(I);F$;" PER ";L$;",LENGTH ";LU(I);F$
590  PRINT "STARTING ";XU(I);F$;" FROM L.H. END ": PRINT
600  NEXT I
610  INPUT "DO YOU WISH TO CHANGE ANYTHING ?";A$: PRINT
620  IF A$ = "Y" THEN 30
630  PRINT "REACTIONS"
640  MSUM = 0:PSUM = 0
650  FOR I = 1 TO NP
660  PSUM = PSUM + PL(I)
670  MSUM = MSUM + PL(I) * XP(I)
680  NEXT I
690  FOR I = 1 TO NU
700  PSUM = PSUM + UL(I) * LU(I)
```

```
710 MSUM = MSUM + UL(I) * LU(I) * (XU(I) + LU(I) / 2)
720 NEXT I
730 R(1) = (MSUM / XR(2) - PSUM) / (XR(1) / XR(2) - 1)
740 R(2) = PSUM - R(1)
750 PRINT : PRINT "LH REACTION = ";R(1);F$;" AT ";XR(1);L$;" FROM L.H.EN
    D ": PRINT
760 PRINT "RH REACTION = ";R(2);F$;" AT ";XR(2);L$;" FROM L.H. END ": PRINT
770 PRINT : PRINT : PRINT : INPUT "DISTANCE FROM L.H. END AT WHICH DEFLE
    CTION IS REQUIRED ?";XB
780 CF = 1.0
790 IF L$ = "M" THEN 820
800 IF L$ < > W$ THEN CF = 0.001
810 GOTO 825
820 IF L$ < > W$ THEN CF = 1000.0
825 A = 0.0:B = 0.0
830 DX = XR(1): GOSUB 1000:F1 = FW
840 DX = XR(2): GOSUB 1000:F2 = FW
850 A = (F1 - F2) / (XR(2) - XR(1)):B =  - A * XR(1) - F1
860 DX = XB: GOSUB 1000:D = FW / EI
870 PRINT : PRINT : PRINT "VERTICAL DEFLECTION AT ";XB;L$;" FROM L.H. EN
    D IS": PRINT
880 PRINT  TAB( 10);CF*D;W$
890 PRINT : PRINT : INPUT "DEFLECTION REQUIRED AT ANY OTHER SECTION ?";A
    $
900 IF A$ = "Y" THEN 770
910 END
1000 REM  SUBROUTINE FOR CALCULATING FW=EI*DEFLECTION
1010 FW = 0.0
1020 FOR I = 1 TO 2
1030 IF DX < = XR(I) THEN 1060
1040 FW = FW - R(I) * ((DX - XR(I)) ^ 3) / 6
1050 NEXT I
1060 IF NP = 0 THEN 1110
1070 FOR I = 1 TO NP
1080 IF DX < = XP(I) THEN 1100
1090 FW = FW + PL(I) * ((DX - XP(I)) ^ 3) / 6
1100 NEXT I
1110 IF NU = 0 THEN 1180
1120 FOR I = 1 TO NU
1130 IF DX < = XU(I) THEN 1170
1140 FW = FW + UL(I) * ((DX - XU(I)) ^ 4) / 24
1150 IF DX < = XU(I) + LU(I) THEN 1170
1160 FW = FW - UL(I) * ((DX - LU(I) - XU(I)) ^ 4) / 24
1170 NEXT I
1180 FW = FW + A * DX + B
1190 RETURN

]
```

Program notes

(1) Lines 10–770   Identical to program given in Example 6.1 except that the, uniform, EI value is required (454).

(2) Lines 780–820   CF is the conversion factor required if deflection units are different from length units.

(3) Lines 825–850   Expression used for deflection is given in Section 6.5.1. A and B are the constants of integration evaluated from $w = 0$ at $x = XR(1)$ and $x = XR(2)$.

(4) Lines 860–910   Calculation and print out of deflection at required point.

The printout below shows the calculation of the deflection 5 m from the left-hand end of the simply supported beam of Figure 6.2 with the uniformly distributed load.

```
VERTICAL DEFLECTION OF A SIMPLY SUPPORTED BEAM BY MACAULAYS METHOD

LENGTH UNITS,M OR MM ?M

FORCE UNITS,N OR KN ?KN

DEFLECTION UNITS,M OR MM ?MM

SPAN OF BEAM ?10

POSITION OF L.H. SUPPORT FROM L.H. END ?0

POSITION OF R.H. SUPPORT FROM L.H. END ?10

CONSISTENT EI VALUE ?1E5

INPUT LOAD DATA IN ANY ORDER

NUMBER OF POINT LOADS ?0

NUMBER OF UNIFORMLY DISTRIBUTED LOADS ?1

FOR U.D.L. NUMBER 1 GIVE

INTENSITY 3

LENGTH 5

DISTANCE OF START OF LOAD FROM L.H. END· 2

DATA SUMMARY

SPAN OF BEAM = 10M

EI = 100000KNM^2

L.H. SUPPORT 0M FROM L.H.END

R.H. SUPPORT 10M FROM L.H. END
```

```
UNIFORMLY DISTRIBUTED LOADS

3KN PER M,LENGTH 5KN
STARTING 2KN FROM L.H. END

DO YOU WISH TO CHANGE ANYTHING ?N

REACTIONS

LH REACTION = 8.25KN AT 0M FROM L.H.END

RH REACTION = 6.75KN AT 10M FROM L.H. END

DISTANCE FROM L.H. END AT WHICH DEFLECTION IS REQUIRED ?5

VERTICAL DEFLECTION AT 5M FROM L.H. END IS

        2.748125MM


DEFLECTION REQUIRED AT ANY OTHER SECTION ?N
```

Note that deflections are positive downwards. Try other sections and the point load case.

Example 6.3 Vertical deflection: Area–moment method

Repeat Example 6.2 using the Area–Moment theorems.

```
5   HOME
10  PRINT "DEFLECTION AND SLOPE FOR SIMPLY"
20  PRINT "SUPPORTED BEAM USING AREA MOMENT"
30  PRINT "THEOREMS - POINT LOADS ONLY ": PRINT : PRINT
40  PRINT "LIMITS FOR THEOREMS ARE XA AND XB,XB>XA": PRINT
50  PRINT "FIRST THEOREM (F) IS": PRINT
60  PRINT "(SLOPE AT XB)-(SLOPE AT XA) ="
70  PRINT "AREA UNDER M/EI DIAGRAM BETWEEN XA & XB": PRINT
80  PRINT "SECOND THEOREM (S) IS": PRINT
90  PRINT "(XB*SLOPE AT XB)-(DEFLECTION AT XB)-"
100  PRINT "-(XA*SLOPE AT XA)+(DEFLECTION AT XA) ="
110  PRINT "MOMENT OF M/EI DIAGRAM BETWEEN XA & XB"
120  PRINT "ABOUT ORIGIN OF X": PRINT : PRINT
130  DIM XP(30),PL(30),BM(30),SL(30),CO(30)
135  D$(1) = "SLOPE AT A ":D$(2) = "DEFLECTION AT A ":D$(3) = "SLOPE AT B
     ":D$(4) = "DEFLECTION AT B "
140  INPUT "LENGTH UNITS,M OR MM ?";L$
150  PRINT : INPUT "FORCE UNITS ,N OR KN ?";F$
160  PRINT : INPUT "DEFLECTION UNITS ,M OR MM ?";W$
170  PRINT : INPUT "LENGTH OF BEAM ?";SP
180  PRINT : INPUT "CONSISTENT EI VALUE ? ";EI
```

```
190 CF = 1.0:XR(1) = 0.0:XR(2) = SP
200 IF L$ = "M" THEN 230
210 IF L$ < > W$ THEN CF = 0.001
220 GOTO 240
230 IF L$ < > W$ THEN CF = 1000
240 PRINT : INPUT "NUMBER OF POINT LOADS ?";NP: PRINT
250 PRINT : PRINT "LOAD DATA SHOULD BE GIVEN IN ORDER OF"
260 PRINT "INCREASING DISTANCE FROM LH END ": PRINT
270 XP(0) = - 0.001:XP(NP + 1) = SP
280 FOR I = 1 TO NP: PRINT "FOR POINT LOAD NUMBER ";I;" GIVE"
290 PRINT : INPUT "MAGNITUDE ";PL(I)
300 PRINT : INPUT "DISTANCE FROM LH END ";XP(I)
310 IF XP(I) > XP(I - 1) THEN 340
320 PRINT : PRINT "LOADS NOT IN CORRECT DISTANCE ORDER !": PRINT
330 GOTO 280
340 NEXT I
350 HOME : PRINT : PRINT "DATA SUMMARY": PRINT
360 PRINT "LENGTH OF BEAM = ";SP;L$: PRINT
370 PRINT "FLEXURAL RIGIDITY EI = ";EI;F$;L$;"^2": PRINT
380 PRINT "DEFLECTION UNITS ARE ";W$: PRINT
390 PRINT "POINT LOADS": PRINT
400 PRINT  TAB( 12);"DISTANCE FROM"; TAB( 30);"MAGNITUDE"
410 PRINT  TAB( 12);" LH END": PRINT
420 FOR I = 1 TO NP: PRINT I; TAB( 12);XP(I); TAB( 30);PL(I): NEXT I
430 PRINT : PRINT "BEAM SIMPLY SUPPORTED AT LH END X=0"
440 PRINT "AND RH END X=SP": PRINT
450 INPUT "DO YOU WISH TO CHANGE ANYTHING Y/N ?";A$
460 IF A$ = "Y" THEN 140
470 PRINT : PRINT "REACTIONS":MSUM = 0.0:PSUM = 0.0
480 FOR I = 1 TO NP:PSUM = PSUM + PL(I):MSUM = MSUM + PL(I) * XP(I): NEXT
    I
490 R1 = (MSUM / XR(2) - PSUM) / (XR(1) / XR(2) - 1):R2 = PSUM - R1
500 PRINT : PRINT "LH REACTION = ";R1;F$: PRINT : PRINT "RH REACTION = "
    ;R2;F$
510 BM(0) = 0.0:BM(NP + 1) = 0.0
520 FOR I = 1 TO NP + 1
530 BM(I) =  - R1 * XP(I)
540 FOR J = 1 TO I - 1:BM(I) = BM(I) + PL(J) * (XP(I) - XP(J)): NEXT J
550 SL(I) = (BM(I) - BM(I - 1)) / (XP(I) - XP(I - 1))
560 CO(I) = (BM(I) * XP(I - 1) - BM(I - 1) * XP(I)) / (XP(I - 1) - XP(I))

570 NEXT I
580 PRINT : INPUT "WHICH THEOREM IS TO BE USED,F/S ?";T$
590 PRINT : PRINT "FIRST LIMIT OF INTEGRATION IS POINT A -"
600 INPUT "GIVE DISTANCE FROM LH SUPPORT XA ";XA
```

```
610  PRINT : PRINT "SECOND LIMIT OF INTEGRATION IS POINT B -"
620  INPUT "GIVE DISTANCE FROM LH SUPPORT XB- ";XB
630  IF XA < = XB THEN 641
640  PRINT : PRINT "XB<XA TRY AGAIN ": GOTO 590
641  FOR I = 1 TO NP + 1
642  IF XA < XP(I - 1) THEN 644
643 LO = I: NEXT I
644  FOR I = 1 TO NP + 1
645  IF XB < XP(I - 1) THEN 650
646  UP = I: NEXT I
650  IF T$ = "S" THEN 870
660  PRINT : PRINT "REQUIRED QUANTITY ?"
670  PRINT : PRINT  TAB( 12);"SLOPE AT A - TYPE 1"
680  PRINT : PRINT  TAB( 12);"SLOPE AT B - TYPE 2"
690  PRINT : INPUT ST: PRINT : PRINT
700  VI = 0.0
710  IF LO < > UP THEN 730
720  VI = 0.5 * SL(LO) * (XB * XB - XA * XA) + CO(LO)*(XB-XA)
730  FOR I = LO TO UP
725 GOTO 800
740  IF I = LO THEN 770
750  IF I = UP THEN 780
760  VI = VI + 0.5 * SL(I) * (XP(I) ^ 2 - XP(I - 1) ^ 2) + CO(I) * (XP(I) -
     XP(I - 1)): GOTO 790
770  VI = VI + 0.5 * SL(I) * (XP(I) ^ 2 - XA * XA) + CO(I) * (XP(I) - XA):
     GOTO 790
780  VI = VI + 0.5 * SL(I) * (XB * XB - XP(I - 1) ^ 2) + CO(I) * (XB - XP(
     I - 1))
790  NEXT I
800  VI = VI / EI
802  IF ST = 1 THEN  INPUT "SLOPE AT B ?";TH
804  IF ST = 2 THEN  INPUT "SLOPE AT A ?";TH
806  IF ST = 1 THEN VI =  - VI
808  TH = TH + VI
820  IF ST = 1 THEN  PRINT "SLOPE AT ";XA;L$;" FROM LH END = ";TH;" RADS"

830  IF ST = 2 THEN  PRINT "SLOPE AT ";XB;L$;" FROM LH END = ";TH;" RADS"

840  PRINT : INPUT "DO YOU WISH TO CONTINUE ? Y/N ";A$
850  IF A$ = "Y" THEN 580
860  GOTO 1190
870  PRINT : PRINT "REQUIRED QUANTITY ?"
880  PRINT : PRINT  TAB( 12);"SLOPE AT A - TYPE 1"
890  PRINT : PRINT  TAB( 12);"DEFLECTION AT ·A - TYPE 2"
900  PRINT : PRINT  TAB( 12);"SLOPE AT B - TYPE 3"
```

```
910  PRINT : PRINT  TAB( 12);"DEFLECTION AT B - TYPE 4"
920  INPUT ST: PRINT : PRINT
930 VI = 0.0
940  IF LO < > UP THEN 960
950 VI = SL(LO) * (XB ^ 3 - XA ^ 3)/3 + 0.5 * CO(LO)*(XB^2 - XA^2)
955  GOTO 1030
960  FOR I = LO TO UP
970  IF I = LO THEN 1000
980  IF I = UP THEN 1010
990  VI = VI + SL(I) * (XP(I) ^ 3 - XP(I - 1) ^ 3) / 3 + 0.5 * CO(I) * (XP
     (I) ^ 2 - XP(I - 1) ^ 2)
995  GOTO 1020
1000 VI = VI + SL(I) * (XP(I) ^ 3 - XA ^ 3) / 3 + 0.5 * CO(I) * (XP(I) ^
     3 - XA ^ 3): GOTO 1020
1010 VI = VI + SL(I) * (XB ^ 3 - XP(I - 1) ^ 3) / 3 + 0.5 * CO(I) * (XB ^
     2 - XP(I - 1) ^ 2)
1020 NEXT I
1030 VI = VI / EI
1050 FOR I = 1 TO 4
1060 IF I = ST THEN 1080
1070 PRINT D$(I);: INPUT Q(I): PRINT
1080 NEXT I
1085 DE = 0.0:TH = 0.0
1090 IF ST = 1 THEN TH = ( - VI + XB * Q(3) - Q(4) + Q(2)) / XA
1100 IF ST = 2 THEN DE = VI - XB * Q(3) + Q(4) + XA * Q(1)
1110 IF ST = 3 THEN TH = (VI - Q(4) + XA * Q(1) - Q(1)) / XB
1120 IF ST = 4 THEN DE =  - VI + XB * Q(3) - XA * Q(1) + Q(2)
1130 DI = XA: IF ST > 2 THEN DI = XB
1140 IF DE = 0.0 THEN 1160
1150 PRINT : PRINT "DEFLECTION AT ";DI;L$;" FROM LH END = ";DE;L$
1152 PRINT : PRINT "(USE THIS VALUE IN FURTHER CALCULATIONS)"
1154 IF CF = 1.0 THEN 1170
1156 PRINT : PRINT "CONVERTED DEFLECTION = ";CF * DE;W$: PRINT : GOTO 11
     70
1160 PRINT : PRINT "SLOPE AT ";DI;L$;" FROM LH END = ";TH;" RADS"
1170 PRINT : INPUT "DO YOU WISH TO CONTINUE ? Y/N ";A$
1180 IF A$ = "Y" THEN 580
1190 END
```

Program notes

(1) Lines 5–120   Program introduction. Note that *only point loads* are considered. This enables the integrals in the theorems shown in Section 6.5.2 to be explicitly calculated using the fact that the bending moment diagram is linear between point loads.

The user decides which theorem to use and between what limits (580). As information on slopes and deflections is carried forward from one application of a theorem to the next (802 and 1070 (see 135)), pen and paper are required if only the VDU is used for output.

(2) Lines 130–45   Data input, summary and change option. Point loads must be supplied in order of increasing distance from left-hand end (250, 260). No overhang of beam is allowed (430, 440).

(3) Lines 470–500   Calculation of reactions.

(4) Lines 510–570   Array BM stores the bending moment at each load point. SL contains the slopes of the line of the bending moment diagram between successive point loads and CO contains the intercept constants for these lines. Thus $y = mx + c \equiv \mathbf{BM} = \mathbf{SL}.x + \mathbf{CO}$.

(5) Lines 580–840   Interactive application of the first theorem (see lines 5–120). LO and UP (641–646) contain the number of the point load below which is the lower limit of integration (XA) and that above which is the upper limit (XB). These are also required in the second theorem (650). In 730–790, integration (summation) of area under bending moment diagram takes place.

(6) Lines 870–1170   Application of the second theorem. In 960–1020, the moment of the bending moment diagram between LO and UP about the origin is calculated using the trapezium shape of the diagram between point loads.

The following printout shows the calculation of the deflection at 5 m from the left-hand support of the simply supported beam of Figure 6.2 with the point loads. If this point is C then the sequence of use of the theorems is ($x_A = 0$).

(1) Second theorem between A and B to give θ_B
(2) First theorem between C and B to give θ_C. In the program, C will be the point 'A'.
(3) Second theorem between A and C to give w_C. In the program, C will be the point 'B'.

In (1) and (2) θ_A is unknown but since it is multiplied by zero, any value can be given.

```
DEFLECTION AND SLOPE FOR SIMPLY
SUPPORTED BEAM USING AREA MOMENT
THEOREMS - POINT LOADS ONLY


LIMITS FOR THEOREMS ARE XA AND XB,XB>XA

FIRST THEOREM (F) IS

(SLOPE AT XB)-(SLOPE AT XA) =
AREA UNDER M/EI DIAGRAM BETWEEN XA & XB
```

SECOND THEOREM (S) IS

(XB*SLOPE AT XB)-(DEFLECTION AT XB)-
-(XA*SLOPE AT XA)+(DEFLECTION AT XA) =
MOMENT OF M/EI DIAGRAM BETWEEN XA & XB
ABOUT ORIGIN OF X

LENGTH UNITS,M OR MM ?M

FORCE UNITS ,N OR KN ?KN

DEFLECTION UNITS ,M OR MM ?MM

LENGTH OF BEAM ?10

CONSISTENT EI VALUE ? 1E5

NUMBER OF POINT LOADS ?2

LOAD DATA SHOULD BE GIVEN IN ORDER OF
INCREASING DISTANCE FROM LH END

FOR POINT LOAD NUMBER 1 GIVE

MAGNITUDE 12

DISTANCE FROM LH END 2
FOR POINT LOAD NUMBER 2 GIVE

MAGNITUDE -8

DISTANCE FROM LH END 7

DATA SUMMARY

LENGTH OF BEAM = 10M

FLEXURAL RIGIDITY EI = 100000KNM^2

DEFLECTION UNITS ARE MM

POINT LOADS

	DISTANCE FROM LH END	MAGNITUDE
1	2	12
2	7	-8

BEAM SIMPLY SUPPORTED AT LH END X=0
AND RH END X=SP

DO YOU WISH TO CHANGE ANYTHING Y/N ?N

REACTIONS

LH REACTION = 7.2KN

RH REACTION = -3.2KN

WHICH THEOREM IS TO BE USED,F/S ?S

FIRST LIMIT OF INTEGRATION IS POINT A -
GIVE DISTANCE FROM LH SUPPORT XA 0

```
SECOND LIMIT OF INTEGRATION IS POINT B -
GIVE DISTANCE FROM LH SUPPORT XB 10

REQUIRED QUANTITY ?

            SLOPE AT A - TYPE 1

            DEFLECTION AT A - TYPE 2

            SLOPE AT B - TYPE 3

            DEFLECTION AT B - TYPE 4
?3


SLOPE AT A ?0

DEFLECTION AT A ?0

DEFLECTION AT B ?0


SLOPE AT 10M FROM LH END = 9.198081E-05 RADS

DO YOU WISH TO CONTINUE ? Y/N Y

WHICH THEOREM IS TO BE USED,F/S ?F

FIRST LIMIT OF INTEGRATION IS POINT A -
GIVE DISTANCE FROM LH SUPPORT XA 5

SECOND LIMIT OF INTEGRATION IS POINT B -
GIVE DISTANCE FROM LH SUPPORT XB 10

REQUIRED QUANTITY ?

            SLOPE AT A - TYPE 1

            SLOPE AT B - TYPE 2
?1


SLOPE AT B ?9.198081E-5
SLOPE AT 5M FROM LH END = -1.40019191E-04 RADS

DO YOU WISH TO CONTINUE ? Y/N Y

WHICH THEOREM IS TO BE USED,F/S ?S

FIRST LIMIT OF INTEGRATION IS POINT A -
GIVE DISTANCE FROM LH SUPPORT XA 0

SECOND LIMIT OF INTEGRATION IS POINT B -
GIVE DISTANCE FROM LH SUPPORT XB 5

REQUIRED QUANTITY ?

            SLOPE AT A - TYPE 1

            DEFLECTION AT A - TYPE 2

            SLOPE AT B - TYPE 3

            DEFLECTION AT B - TYPE 4
?4
```

```
SLOPE AT A ?0

DEFLECTION AT A ?0

SLOPE AT B ?-1.48019191E-4


DEFLECTION AT 5M FROM LH END = 1.00095949E-04M

(USE THIS VALUE IN FURTHER CALCULATIONS)

CONVERTED DEFLECTION = .100095949MM


DO YOU WISH TO CONTINUE ? Y/N N
```

Check this output with the Macaulay program of Example 6.2.

Example 6.4 Vertical deflection: virtual work method

Repeat the calculation of Example 6.3 using the method of virtual work.

```
10  REM  PROGRAM CALCULATES VERTICAL DEFLECTION OF  A BEAM AT A SPECIFIC
        SECTION XB DUE TO POINT LOADS USING A VIRTUAL WORK METHOD
20  DIM BM(30),XP(30),PL(30)
30  HOME : PRINT : PRINT "DETERMINATION OF VERTICAL DEFLECTION OF A SIMPL
        Y SUPPORTED BEAM WITH SEVERAL POINT LOADS USING VIRTUAL WORK"
40  PRINT : INPUT "LENGTH UNITS,M OR MM ?";L$
50  PRINT : INPUT "FORCE UNITS,N OR KN ?";F$
60  PRINT : INPUT "LENGTH OF BEAM ?";SP
70  PRINT : INPUT "CONSISTENT EI VALUE ?";EI
80  PRINT : INPUT "DEFLECTION UNITS,M OR MM ?";W$
90  CF = 1.0
95  XR(1) = 0.0:XR(2) = SP
100  IF L$ = "M" THEN 130
110  IF L$ < > W$ THEN CF = 0.001
120  GOTO 150
130  IF L$ < > W$ THEN CF = 1000
150  PRINT : INPUT "NUMBER OF POINT LOADS ?";NP: PRINT
160  REM  NO UDL INCLUDED IN THIS PROGRAM
170 NU = 0
180  PRINT : PRINT "LOAD DATA SHOULD BE PRESENTED IN ORDER OF INCREASING
        DISTANCE FROM L.H. END": PRINT
190  XP(0) = 0
200  FOR I = 1 TO NP
210  PRINT "FOR POINT LOAD NUMBER ";I;" GIVE"
220  PRINT : INPUT "MAGNITUDE ";PL(I)
```

```
230  PRINT : INPUT "DISTANCE FROM LEFT HAND END";XP(I)
240  IF XP(I) > XP(I - 1) THEN 270
250  PRINT : PRINT "LOADS NOT IN CORRECT DISTANCE ORDER,TRY AGAIN": PRINT

260  GOTO 190
270  NEXT I
275  XP(NP + 1) = SP
280  PRINT : INPUT "VERTICAL DEFLECTION OR SLOPE REQUIRED ,D OR R ?";D$
290  PRINT : INPUT "AT WHAT DISTANCE FROM THE L.H. END OF THE BEAM ?";XB
300  PRINT : INPUT "NUMBER OF INTERVALS FOR NUMERICAL INTEGRATION ?";TT
310  HOME : PRINT : PRINT "DATA SUMMARY ": PRINT
320  PRINT "LENGTH OF BEAM = ";SP;L$: PRINT
330  PRINT "FLEXURAL RIGIDITY EI = ";EI;F$;L$;"^2": PRINT
340  PRINT "DEFLECTION UNITS ARE ";W$: PRINT
350  PRINT "POINT LOADS ": PRINT
360  PRINT  TAB( 12);"DISTANCE FROM"; TAB( 30);"MAGNITUDE"
370  PRINT  TAB( 12);" L.H.END": PRINT
380  FOR I = 1 TO NP
390  PRINT I; TAB( 12);XP(I); TAB( 30);PL(I): NEXT I
400  S$ = "VERTICAL DEFLECTION"
410  IF D$ = "R" THEN S$ = "SLOPE"
420  PRINT : PRINT S$;" REQUIRED AT ";XB;L$;" FROM LH END": PRINT
430  PRINT "NO. OF INTERVALS FOR NUM. INTEGRATION=";TT
440  PRINT : INPUT "DO YOU WISH TO CHANGE ANYTHING ?";A$
450  IF A$ = "Y" THEN 30
460  PRINT : PRINT "REACTIONS"
470  MSUM = 0.0:PSUM = 0.0
480  FOR I = 1 TO NP
490  PSUM = PSUM + PL(I):MSIM = MSUM + PL(I) * XP(I)
500  NEXT I
510  R(1) = (MSUM / XR(2) - PSUM) / (XR(1) / XR(2) - 1):R(2) = PSUM - R(1)

520  PRINT : PRINT "LH REACTION = ";R(1);F$;" AT ";XR(1);L$;" FROM L.H. E
     ND": PRINT
530  PRINT "RH REACTION = ";R(2);F$;" AT ";XR(2);L$;" FROM R.H. END": PRINT

540  XM = XR(1)
550  GOSUB 2000:BM(0) = MO
560  FOR I = 1 TO NP
570  XM = XP(I): GOSUB 2000:BM(I) = MO
580  NEXT I
590  XM = XR(2)
600  GOSUB 2000:BM(NP + 1) = MO
610 DA = XB / SP - 1:DB = 0.0:DC = XB / SP:DD =  - XB
```

```
620 RA = 1 / SP:RB = 0.0:RC = 1 / SP:RD = - 1.0
630 DE = 0.0:AA = 0.0:PP = 0.0
640  FOR I = 1 TO NP + 1
650 BB = (BM(I) - BM(I - 1)) / (XP(I) - XP(I - 1))
660 CC = BM(I - 1) - BB * XP(I - 1)
670  IF XP(I) > XB THEN 740
680 LI = XP(I - 1):LJ = XP(I)
690  IF D$ = "R" THEN 710
700 QQ = DA:RR = DB: GOTO 720
710 QQ = RA:RR = RB
720  GOSUB 6200
730 DE = DE + VI: GOTO 930
740  IF XP(I - 1) < XB THEN 810
750 LI = XP(I - 1):LJ = XP(I)
760  IF D$ = "R" THEN 780
770 QQ = DC:RR = DD: GOTO 790

780 QQ = RC:RR = RD
790  GOSUB 6200
800 DE = DE + VI: GOTO 930
810 LI = XP(I - 1):LJ = XB
820  IF D$ = "R" THEN 840
830 QQ = DA:RR = DB: GOTO 850
840 QQ = RA:RR = RB
845  PRINT LI;" ";LJ;" ";VI: INPUT A$
850  GOSUB 6200
860 DE = DE + VI
870 LI = XB:LJ = XP(I)
880  IF D$ = "R" THEN 900
890 QQ = DC:RR = DD: GOTO 910
900 QQ = RC:RR = RD
910  GOSUB 6200
920 DE = DE + VI
930  NEXT I
935 DE = DE / EI
940  PRINT : PRINT
950  IF D$ = "R" THEN 990
960 PRINT "VERTICAL DEFLECTION AT ";XB;L$;" FROM LH END"
975  PRINT : PRINT  TAB( 20);CF * DE;W$
980  GOTO 1010
990  PRINT "SLOPE OF BEAM ";XB;L$;" FROM LH END"
1000  PRINT : PRINT  TAB( 20);DE;" RADIANS"
1010  END
2000  REM  SUBROUTINE FOR BM AND SF AT XM
2010 MO = 0.0:SF = 0.0
```

```
2020   IF XM < = XR(1) THEN 2060
2030   MO = MO + R(1) * (XM - XR(1)):SF = SF + XR(1)
2040   IF XM < = XR(2) THEN 2060
2050   MO = MO + R(2) * (XM - XR(2)):SF = SF + XR(2)
2060   IF NP = 0 THEN 2110
2070   FOR I = 1 TO NP
2080   IF XM < = XP(I) THEN 2110
2090   MO = MO - PL(I) * (XM - XP(I)):SF = SF - XP(I)
2100   NEXT I
2110   IF NU = 0 THEN 2170
2120   FOR I = 1 TO NU
2130   IF XM < = XU(I) THEN 2170
2140   IF XM < XU(I) + XL(I) THEN 2160
2150   MO = MO = UL(I) * LU(I) * (XM - XU(I) = 0.5 * LU(I)):SF = SF - ·UL(I)
           * LU(I): GOTO 2160
2155   MO = MO - 0.5 * UL(I) * (XM - XU(I)) * (XM - XU(I)):SF = SF - UL(I) *
           (XM - XU(I))
2160   NEXT I
2165   REM  SIGN CHANGE FOR SIGN CONVENTION
2170   MO = - MO:SF = - SF
2180   RETURN
6200   REM   TRAPEZOIDAL INTEGRATION-DOUBLE FUNCTION
6210   TI = (LJ - LI) / TT
6220   VI = 0.0
6230   FF = (AA * LI * LI + BB * LI + CC) * (PP * LI * LI + QQ * LI + RR)
6240   FOR IT = 1 TO TT
6250   XX = LI + IT * TI
6260   FB = FF
6270   FF = (AA * XX * XX + BB * XX + CC) * (PP * XX * XX + QQ * XX + RR)
6280   VI = VI + 0.5 * (FB + FF) * TI
6290   NEXT IT
6300   RETURN
```

Program notes

(1) Lines 10–450   Data input, summary and change option. Slope or deflection can be calculated (280) and trapezoidal numerical integration is used to evaluate the internal virtual work (300 and 6200–6300).

(2) Lines 460–530   Calculation and print out of reactions. Note that only point loads are considered and no overhang of the beam is permitted.

(3) Lines 540–600   Calculation of bending moments at each of the point loads. These are stored in BM.

(4) Lines 610–930   Evaluation of $DE = \int_{\text{span}} M^* M\, x$ (note line 935; $DE = DE/EI$), the diagrams of Figure 6.6 show the form of M^* and M.

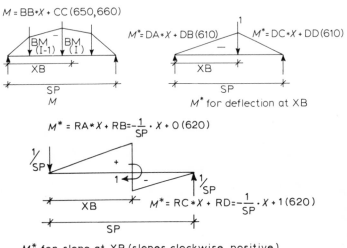

Figure 6.6

Note that slopes will be clockwise positive.

The integral is divided into sub-integrals whose limits are the positions of successive point loads. There are NP + 1 of these and they are evaluated in the FOR loop from 640–930. Each sub-integral is of two linear functions multiplied together. The constants for these functions are shown in the figure and these constants are transferred to the numerical integration subroutine (6200).

For sub-integrals to the left of that including XB(670), evaluation is carried out in 680–730. Sub-integrals to the right of that including XB(740) are evaluated in 750–700. The special case of that sub-integral containing XB (where a sudden change of slope or value of M^* is encountered) is dealt with in 810–920.

The printout below shows the evaluation of the vertical deflection at $x = 5$ m for the simply supported beam of Figure 6.2, with point loads.

```
FORCE UNITS,N OR KN ?KN

LENGTH OF BEAM ?10

CONSISTENT EI VALUE ?1E5

DEFLECTION UNITS,M OR MM ?MM

NUMBER OF POINT LOADS ?2


LOAD DATA SHOULD BE PRESENTED IN ORDER OF INCREASING DISTANCE FROM L.H. END

FOR POINT LOAD NUMBER 1 GIVE

MAGNITUDE 12

DISTANCE FROM LEFT HAND END2
FOR POINT LOAD NUMBER 2 GIVE

MAGNITUDE -8

DISTANCE FROM LEFT HAND END7

VERTICAL DEFLECTION OR SLOPE REQUIRED ,D OR R ?D

AT WHAT DISTANCE FROM THE L.H. END OF THE BEAM ?5

NUMBER OF INTERVALS FOR NUMERICAL INTEGRATION ?20

DATA SUMMARY

LENGTH OF BEAM = 10M

FLEXURAL RIGIDITY EI = 100000KNM^2

DEFLECTION UNITS ARE MM

POINT LOADS

            DISTANCE FROM                    MAGNITUDE
             L.H.END

1           2                       12
2           7                       -8


VERTICAL DEFLECTION REQUIRED AT 5M FROM LH END

NO. OF INTERVALS FOR NUM. INTEGRATION=20

DO YOU WISH TO CHANGE ANYTHING ?N

REACTIONS

LH REACTION = 7.2KN AT 0M FROM L.H. END

RH REACTION = -3.2KN AT 10M FROM R.H. END


VERTICAL DEFLECTION AT 5M FROM LH END

                .0997500005MM
```

PROBLEMS

(6.1) Use the program given in Example 6.1 to evaluate the bending moment and shear force at equal intervals along the beam shown in Figure 6.2 with both the point loading and the uniformly distributed load. What size of interval is required in order to draw the bending moment and shear force diagrams with confidence and accuracy?

(6.2) Use the program of Example 6.1 to check BM and SF diagrams for beams and loading of your own or from other sources. At what points on your diagrams is a larger concentration of values required? Modify the program to give values at equal intervals within a small limited length of beam (1100–1160).

(6.3) How would you use the modified program of Problem (6.2) to find the optimum values of the bending moment?

(6.4) Carry out hand checks on the results of Examples 6.2, 6.3 and 6.4. Using the Macaulay Method program (Example 6.2) as a standard compare the time taken to calculate displacements by the area–moment and virtual work methods. What are the advantages of these latter two methods?

(6.5) For a simply supported beam of span 10 m, say, and uniform $EI = 10^5 \, \text{kN m}^2$, apply a unit vertical load at 3 m from the left-hand support A and calculate the deflection at a point 5 m from the left-hand support. Repeat the calculation with the unit load applied 5 m from the left-hand end and the deflection measured at 3 m from A. The values are identical. Do the same calculation with two other points and observe a similar conclusion. Furthermore, apply a unit *moment* at A and calculate the *vertical deflection* at 3 m, 5 m and 7 m from A. Note the direction of these deflections. Now add *unit loads* successively at 3 m, 5 m and 7 m in directions indicated by the previously calculated deflections and compute the *slope* at A. Again the values are identical.

These results demonstrate the reciprocal theorem for an elastic body such as a beam. The deflection or rotation at a section X due to a unit load or moment at a section Y is equal to the deflection or rotation at Y when the same load or moment is applied at X with due consideration of the directions of the applied loads. The theorem similarly deals with truss member forces, stresses, strains and other linearly dependent quantities within the elastic range.

(6.6) Modify the virtual work program (Example 6.4) to include uniformly distributed loads. It is probably easiest to start with a uniformly distributed load covering the whole span. Point loads can also be applied, the M diagram now being parabolic between each load. The intensity of the udl must be input (at around 270), reactions modified (510) and BB, CC and now AA computed (650 and 660).

Uniformly distributed loads of length less than the span, present more problems. It may be best to deal with them separately from the point loads, superposing the separate displacements. Thus a new integration section (540–930) will be required.

(6.7) Carry out a similar modification to Problem (6.6) of the Area–Moment program (Example 6.3) to include uniformly distributed loads. In this program the integrals are explicitly evaluated in lines 760–780 and 990–1010 and these should be changed from linear to parabolic function integrals.

(6.8) The main advantage of the virtual work method is that non-uniform beams can be analysed with comparative ease. An expression (linear, parabolic, etc.) for EI can be established within each sub-integral for numerical integration (630–930). The constants of these expressions are transferred to the Trapezoidal integration subroutine (6200) where FF is changed from $FF = F1_*F2$ to $FF = F1_*F2/EI$. Line 935 is now no longer required.

Carry out these changes for a linear variation of EI (what does this mean geometrically?) and analyse a few simple examples that can be checked by hand.

(6.9) What changes are required to enable the area–moment and virtual work method programs to analyse cantilever beams? The reactions are different but are there any other changes? Carry out the conversion and test the program against hand calculations.

Chapter 7

Influence line diagrams

ESSENTIAL THEORY

7.1 Introduction

Influence line diagrams show how the bending moment, shear force or deflection at a section of a beam or the force in a member of a truss or deflection of a joint vary as a unit load passes across the structure. Influence line diagrams (ILDs) may be drawn for any other quantity of interest (such as the stress at a point within a structure) and for statically determinate or indeterminate structures. As the principle of superposition (see Section 2.3) is usually invoked when using ILDs they are usually constructed for quantities linearly dependent on loading. We shall, of course, deal only with statically determinate beams and trusses.

Initially some difficulty may be experienced in visualising ILDs. In the case of bending moments and beam deflections it may help to think of the ILDs as the opposite of the Bending Moment Diagram or Deflection Curve. These latter diagrams are plots of the bending moment or deflection at *every* section of the beam due to a given *fixed set of loads*. Values are *plotted* at the *section* to which *they refer*. The ILD shows the bending moment or deflection at a *single* section of the beam as a unit load of *varying position* moves across the beam. Values are plotted *at each position* of the unit load but are those at the single chosen section.

ILDs are usually drawn for points or sections of the structure which are likely to carry the largest bending moment, stress or deflection. These are 'critical' sections for the designer who has to consider moving point and uniformly distributed loads representing the movement of traffic, pedestrians, etc. To draw bending moment diagrams, shear force diagrams and deflection curves for every possible position of these loads would not only be very time consuming, but would generate much unwanted information.

A full discussion of the application of ILDs is beyond the scope of this book but some simple applications are given.

7.2 ILDs for simply supported beams

The influence line diagram for the bending moment (M), shear force (S) or deflection (w) at a section on simply supported beam is a graph of the bending moment, shear force or deflection induced at the section by a unit load as it moves across the beam. These induced values are plotted at the current position of the unit load.

Figure 7.1(a) shows the simply supported beam AB, span L, with section C distance a from the left-hand support A. With the unit load at a point x from A, the vertical reactions are, $R_A = 1 - x/L$ and $R_B = x/L$. Thus when,

$$x \leqslant a \quad M_C = \frac{-(L-a)x}{L} \text{ and } S_C = \frac{-x}{L}$$

$$x \geqslant a \quad M_C = -a\left\{1 - \frac{x}{L}\right\} \text{ and } S_C = 1 - \frac{x}{L}$$

Note that these are the values of bending moment and shear force induced at C due to the unit load at x. The expressions are linear in x and are plotted in Figures 7.1(a) and 7.1(b) to form the influence lines diagrams.

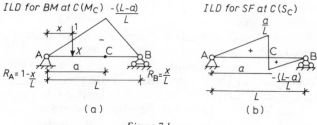

$$(a) \qquad\qquad (b)$$

Figure 7.1

Note how the peak values are recorded without units although these are implied. Also, although the ILD for M_C is similar to a BMD for a fixed point load at C, the ILD for S_C bears no similarity to a shear force diagram for point loading. As might be expected, there is no relationship between these diagrams.

The influence line diagram for deflection at C (w_C) could also be determined by placing the unit load at a general point X, x from A and hence obtaining an expression for the deflection at C in terms of x. Alternatively, using the reciprocal theorem (Problem (6.5)) it can be seen that the deflection at C due to the unit load at X is equal to the deflection at X due to the unit load at C. Thus the deflection curve obtained by placing the unit load at C will be the ILD for w_C! This has only the small advantage of somewhat simplifying the calculation in this simple example. However, in more complex structures this fact greatly reduces the amount of computation required for the deflection ILD.

Using any of the methods described in Chapter 6 it can be shown that the deflection curve for a unit load at C on the simply supported beam of Figure 7.1(a), is

$$w = \frac{L^2}{6}\left\{1 - \frac{a}{L}\right\}x - \frac{(L-a)^3}{6L}x - \left\{1 - \frac{a}{L}\right\}\frac{x^3}{6} + \frac{[x-a]^3}{6}$$

where $[x-a]$ is a Macaulay term (see Section 6.5.1). This deflection curve will be the ILD for w_C.

7.3 Application of ILDs

If a set of fixed point loads of magnitude $P_1, P_2, \ldots, P_n$ are applied to the beam at distances $x_1, x_2, \ldots, x_n$ from A, then using superposition, the total induced moment at C is,

$$M_C(\text{total}) = P_1 v(x_1) + P_2 v(x_2) + \ldots + P_n v(x_n) = \sum_{i=1}^{n} P_i v(x_i)$$

with appropriate units. $v(x_i)$ is the value of the ordinate at x_i of the ILD for the moment at C. S. Similar expressions are used for $S_C(\text{total})$ and $w_C(\text{total})$.

If a uniformly distributed load of intensity q is applied over a length of the beam from x_1 to x_2, then the total effect at C is given by,

$$M_C(\text{total}) = S_C \text{total}) = w_C(\text{total}) = \int_{x_1}^{x_2} qv(x)\,dx$$

$$= q \times (\text{area under the ILD from between } x_1 \text{ and } x_2)$$

Here $v(x)$ is the appropriate ILD function.

As mentioned in the introduction, the designer usually chooses a critical section ($a = L/2$ for bending moment and deflection, $a = 0$ or L for shear force for a simply supported beam) and finds the maximum effect due to the expected loading. This will consist of the *Dead Loading* (DL) and the *Live Loading* (LL). The Dead Loading is the load due to the self weight of the structure which is generally an equivalent uniformly distributed load, intensity q_D, over the complete structure. The Live Loading is usually that due to moving traffic and pedestrians which is idealised as trains of point and uniformly distributed loads passing across the structure.

The calculation of maximum effects with these load trains is beyond the scope of this book but the simple case of a LL which is a uniformly distributed load of intensity q_L and of length greater than the span of the beam, illustrates the principles. In all cases, the effect of the DL is simply the value of the equivalent uniformly distributed load, q_D, multiplied by the total area under the ILD. As the LL is longer than the span, it may occupy three positions as it moves across the beam. Firstly, the 'front' end may partially cover the span, secondly the load may completely cover the span and thirdly the 'rear' end may partially cover the span. In the first and last positions only parts of the ILD are covered. As these parts may be positive or negative, the total effect, which is the sum of the LL and DL effects, can change appreciably.

In the case of the beam shown in Figure 7.1, the value of M_C due to the Dead Load will be, for q_D in kN/m and distances in m,

$$M_C^{DL} = q_D \cdot \tfrac{1}{2} \cdot L \cdot \left(-\frac{(L-a)a}{L} \right) = -q_D \frac{(L-a)}{2} a \text{ kNm}$$

As the ILD is negative everywhere, this will be the minimum value of M_C. Clearly, the maximum moment induced by the LL, q_L, will occur when it completely covers the span and thus the maximum value of M_C is

$$M_C^{max} = M_C^{DL} + M_C^{LL} = -\frac{(q_D + q_L)(L-a)}{2} a \text{ kNm}$$

The shear force at C, due to the Dead Load, has the value

$$S_C^{DL} = q_D \left[\tfrac{1}{2} \cdot a \cdot \frac{a}{L} - \tfrac{1}{2} \frac{(L-a)(L-a)}{L} \right] = \frac{q_D}{2L}[a^2 - (L-a)^2] \text{ kN}$$

As the LL moves onto the span from A to B, this value is increased until the front end of the LL is at C. The LL now covers the beam from A to C with the rest of it as yet to move onto the span. The shear force then induced at C is,

$$S_C^{LL+} = \frac{q_L}{2} \cdot \frac{a^2}{L} \text{ kN}$$

When the front end of the LL passes B, the load completely covers the span and the induced shear force is

$$S_C^{LL} = \frac{q_L}{2L}[a^2 - (L-a)^2] \text{ kN}$$

Eventually, the rear end of the LL reaches C when the negative section CB of the ILD is covered. The shear force induced is then

$$S_C^{LL-} = \frac{-q_L}{2}\frac{(L-a)^2}{L} \text{ kN}$$

Thus, the maximum induced shear force is,

$$S_C^{max} = S_C^{DL} + S_C^{LL+} = \frac{(q_D+q_L)}{2L}a^2 - \frac{q_D(L-a)^2}{2L} \text{ kN}$$

The minimum value is

$$S_C^{min} = S_C^{DL} + S_C^{LL-} = \frac{q_D a^2}{2L} - (q_D+q_L)\frac{(L-a)^2}{2L} \text{ kN}$$

and an intermediate value, when the span is completely covered by the LL, is

$$S_C = S_C^{DL} + S_C^{LL}\frac{(q_D+q_L)}{2L}[a^2-(L-a)^2] \text{ kN}$$

7.4 ILDs for hinged beams and trusses

7.4.1 Hinged beams

A hinged beam is one with several spans but with sufficient hinges inserted to ensure statical determinancy. If there are n spans, $n-1$ hinges are required. A two span example is shown in Figure 7.2. Although the bending moment is zero at a hinge, shear force can be transmitted across. Usually ILDs are required for reactions at supports as well as the shear force, bending moment and deflection at selected sections. As the hinged beam is statically determinate, a similar process for ILD construction to that used with the simply supported beam may be used. General expressions for the various quantities in terms of x, the position of the unit load, may be developed using the usual equilibrium equations.

This could be a tedious process but the principle of virtual work can

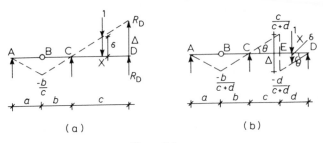

Figure 7.2

be used to give the shape of an ILD very rapidly. Thus, if the ILD for the reaction R_D of the two span hinged beam of Figure 7.2 is required, let us assume that this is an external force applied in a controlled manner and that D may now move vertically. The only other external loading is the unit load at some position X. If R_D is moved through a distance Δ, the beam (now, in fact, a mechanism) will move rigidly as shown. Note that there is only one such possible movement without applying other forces and that supports may act downward as well as upwards.

The unit load moves through a distance δ against its line of action and the work equation is

$$\text{External virtual work} = R_D.\Delta - 1.\delta = \text{Internal virtual work} = 0$$

Thus $R_D = \delta/\Delta$ and the ordinate of the deflected shape of the beam is proportional to the value of R_D induced by a unit load at that ordinate (negative along ABC indicating that R acts downwards). The shape of the ILD for R_D is thus that of the deflected beam as shown in Figure 7.2(a). All that is required is to establish the scale of the diagram by placing a unit load at the peaks and determining the values from equilibrium. In this case, as the ILD consists of straight lines, only one value is required, the rest may be determined from geometry.

A similar approach has been used to find the ILD for the shear force at E in Figure 7.2(b). The beam is cut at E and the two sides of the cut are moved so that S_E does work $S_E.\Delta$ and the net work of the moment M_E is zero. For this to be so, CE and ED must remain parallel which ensures that on one side of the cut the moment does work $-M_E\theta$ and on the other $+M_E\theta$. Again the virtual work balance shows that the shape of the ILD is that of the deflected beam as shown, with peak values determined by placing unit loads at these points and calculating S_E in the usual manner.

It is well worth the reader's time to check these two ILDs by using conventional equilibrium methods. The philosophy behind the surprisingly simple yet powerful results obtained by using virtual work methods is often difficult to grasp in the early stages and for simple two span and three span hinged beams there is little advantage obtained from using it. However, with beams of many spans and with statically indeterminate beams (for which the philosophy still holds) computation is greatly reduced using virtual work methods.

The virtual work concept has been used in the program that follows later to enable you to draw ILDs for two and three span hinged beams. Use this program to test your ability to draw ILD shapes using virtual work. Check the final diagram using conventional equilibrium methods and in this way you will increase your knowledge and understanding of structural behaviour.

ILDs for hinged beam deflection can be shown to be the deflection curves resulting from a unit load applied at the appropriate section.

7.4.2 Trusses

Influence line diagrams for member forces and joint deflections may be constructed by equilibrium or virtual work methods. Since loading may only be applied at joints, the unit load need only be applied to each joint along the loading path. The force in the appropriate member can be calculated at each of these positions to give points on the ILD which can be joined with straight lines.

Obviously, in simple cases with a few members, these member forces may be calculated quite quickly using the method of sections (see Section 4.8) and there is little advantage in using the virtual work method described later. ILDs for joint deflections are constructed from the deflections of the loading path due to unit load applied in the required direction of the required joint.

Since computers take very little longer to calculate all the member forces due to a unit load in each direction at each joint than for a single application of the unit load, the program supplied does just that. This enables the influence line diagrams to be drawn for all the member forces if required. This complete information also helps to compute data for deflection ILDs.

Virtual work can again be used to find the shape of member force ILDs. The member X in the truss shown in Figure 7.3(a) is replaced by an equivalent external force couple F_X (either tensile or compressive) which is moved through a relative distance Δ. The rest of the truss moves rigidly (in the statically determinate case) and the unit load on the loading path moves through δ as in Figure 7.3(b). A virtual work equation shows that the deflected shape of the load path members and joints (ABCDE) is the shape of the ILD for F_X. Peak values are obtained from the method of sections.

In practice, such a shape is found by drawing GC increased (or decreased) in length as a base line (any orientation, though that given

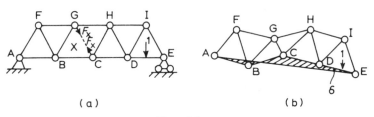

(a)   (b)

Figure 7.3

will do) and, using ruler and compass to plot the positions of all the other joints. This can, of course, only be done in the statically determinate case since then no forces develop in the members due to the extension of GC. Joining A and E on this deflection diagram will give the base line for the ILD. They can, in fact, be very rapidly sketched once you have gained experience but beware, spurious displacements can occur when the displacement of F_X is large. These are quickly revealed when peak values are determined.

WORKED EXAMPLES

Example 7.1 ILDs for simply supported beam

Draw the ILDs for bending moment, shear force and deflection at various sections along a simply supported beam.

```
10  HOME : PRINT "INFLUENCE LINE DIAGRAMS FOR SIMPLY"
20  PRINT "SUPPORTED BEAM"
25  DIM DI(30),X(30)
30  PRINT : INPUT "SPAN OF BEAM ? ";SP
35  PRINT : INPUT "LENGTH UNITS M OR MM ?";L$
40  PRINT : INPUT "CONSISTENT EI VALUE ?";EI
50  PRINT : PRINT "DISTANCE FROM LH SUPPORT OF SECTION AT"
60  INPUT "WHICH ILD IS REQUIRED ?";XB
70  PRINT : INPUT "ILD FOR BM SF OR DEFLECTION B/S/D ?";I$
75  XS(2) = SP:XS(1) = 0.0:X(1) = 0.0:X(2) = XB:X(3) = SP
80  IF I$ = "D" THEN 300
85  IF I$ = "B" THEN 210
95  VP = XB / XS(2):V(1) = 0.0:V(2) = VP:V(4) = 0.0
97  PRINT : PRINT : PRINT
100 PRINT : PRINT "VALUES FOR ILD FOR SHEAR FORCE AT"
105 PRINT : PRINT XB;L$;" FROM LH SUPPORT"
110 PRINT : PRINT "DISTANCE FROM"; TAB( 20);"IL VALUE"
120 PRINT  TAB( 2);"LH SUPPORT": PRINT
130 FOR I = 1 TO 3
140 IF X(I) = XB THEN 160
150 PRINT X(I); TAB( 20);V(I): PRINT : GOTO 180
160 PRINT X(I);"-"; TAB( 20);V(I): PRINT
170 PRINT X(I);"+"; TAB( 20);V(I) - 1.0: PRINT
180 NEXT I
190 PRINT : INPUT "ILD FOR BENDING MOMENT REQUIRED Y/N ?";A$
200 IF A$ = "N" THEN 490
210 VP =  - XB * (XS(2) - XB) / XS(2):V(1) = 0.0:V(2) = VP:V(3) = 0.0
220 PRINT : PRINT : PRINT
225 PRINT : PRINT "VALUES FOR ILD FOR BENDING MOMENT AT"
```

```
230  PRINT : PRINT XB;L$;" FROM LH SUPPORT"
240  PRINT : PRINT "DISTANCE FROM"; TAB( 20);"IL VALUE"
250  PRINT  TAB( 2);"LH SUPPORT": PRINT
260  FOR I = 1 TO 3
270  PRINT X(I); TAB( 20);V(I): PRINT
280  NEXT I
290  GOTO 490
300  C = (1.0 - XB / XS(2)) * XS(2) * XS(2) / 6 - ((XS(2) - XB) ^ 3) / (6 *
     XS(2))
310  DI(0) = 0.0
320  FOR I = 1 TO 10
330  X(I) = I * XB / 10
340  DI(I) = C * X(I) - (1.0 - XB / XS(2)) * (X(I) ^ 3) / 6: NEXT I
350  FOR I = 11 TO 20
360  X(I) = XB + (I - 10) * (XS(2) - XB) / 10
370  DI(I) = C * X(I) + ((X(I) - XB) ^ 3) / 6 - (1.0 - XB / XS(2)) * (X(I)
     ^ 3) / 6
380  NEXT I
382  FOR I = 1 TO 20:DI(I) = DI(I) / EI: NEXT I
385  PRINT : PRINT : PRINT
390  PRINT : PRINT "VALUES FOR ILD FOR DEFLECTION AT"
400  PRINT : PRINT XB;L$;" FROM LH SUPPORT"
410  PRINT : PRINT "DISTANCE FROM"; TAB( 20);"IL VALUE"
420  PRINT  TAB( 2);"LH SUPPORT"
425  J = 0
430  FOR I = 0 TO 20:J = J + 1
450  PRINT X(I); TAB( 20);DI(I): PRINT
460  IF J < 8 THEN 480
470  INPUT "PRESS ANY KEY TO CONTINUE";A$:J = 0: PRINT
480  NEXT I
490  PRINT : INPUT "ANY MORE ILDS REQUIRED Y/N ?";A$: PRINT
500  IF A$ = "Y" THEN 50
510  END
```

Program notes

(1) The program evaluates and prints out the principal values of the diagrams as shown in Figure 7.1 and discussed in Section 7.2.

(2) Lines 10–70   Data input.

(3) Lines 95–180   Calculation and printout of principal values of the I:D for shear force. Note that at the section to be considered, XB from left-hand end, two values are printed at XB – and XB +; just to the left and just to the right of the section (140–180),

(4) Lines 190–280   Calculation and printout of principal values of the ILD for bending moment (see Figure 7.1).

(5) Lines 300–480   Using the expression for w given in Section 7.2, ten equally spaced values of the ILD for displacement to the left of the chosen section (320–340) and to the right of the section (350–380) are calculated and printed out (430–480).

A typical output is shown below.

```
INFLUENCE LINE DIAGRAMS FOR SIMPLY
SUPPORTED BEAM

SPAN OF BEAM ? 10

LENGTH UNITS M OR MM ?M

CONSISTENT EI VALUE ?1E5

DISTANCE FROM LH SUPPORT OF SECTION AT
WHICH ILD IS REQUIRED ?2

ILD FOR BM SF OR DEFLECTION B/S/D ?S


VALUES FOR ILD FOR SHEAR FORCE AT

2M FROM LH SUPPORT

DISTANCE FROM        IL VALUE
  LH SUPPORT

0                    0

2-                   .2

2+                   -.8

10                   0


ILD FOR BENDING MOMENT REQUIRED Y/N ?Y


VALUES FOR ILD FOR BENDING MOMENT AT

2M FROM LH SUPPORT

DISTANCE FROM        IL VALUE
  LH SUPPORT

0                    0

2                    -1.6

10                   0


ANY MORE ILDS REQUIRED Y/N ?Y


DISTANCE FROM LH SUPPORT OF SECTION AT
WHICH ILD IS REQUIRED ?2
```

```
ILD FOR BM SF OR DEFLECTION B/S/D ?D


VALUES FOR ILD FOR DEFLECTION AT

2M FROM LH SUPPORT

DISTANCE FROM        IL VALUE
  LH SUPPORT
  0                    0

  .2                   9.58933333E-06

  .4                   1.91146667E-05

  .6                   2.8512E-05

  .8                   3.77173333E-05

  1                    4.66666667E-05

  1.2                  5.5296E-05

  1.4                  6.35413333E-05

PRESS ANY KEY TO CONTINUE

  1.6                  7.13386666E-05

  1.8                  7.8624E-05

  2                    8.53333333E-05

  2.8                  1.05984E-04

  3.6                  1.17418667E-04

  4.4                  1.20661333E-04

  5.2                  1.16736E-04

  6                    1.06666667E-04

PRESS ANY KEY TO CONTINUE

  6.8                  9.14773327E-05

  7.6                  7.21919993E-05

  8.4                  4.98346662E-05

  9.2                  2.54293317E-05

  10                  -5.96046448E-13


ANY MORE ILDS REQUIRED Y/N ?N
```

Example 7.2 ILDs for two-span hinged beams

Use the program listed below to draw the ILDs for reaction and the bending moment and shear force at various sections along hinged, two-span beams of the type shown in Figure 7.2.

```
5  HOME : PRINT : PRINT
10  PRINT "DATA FOR ILDS FOR TWO SPAN"
20  PRINT : PRINT "HINGED BEAMS - PEAK VALUES ONLY"
35  PRINT : INPUT "LENGTH UNITS ?";L$
50  PRINT : INPUT "LENGTH OF LH SPAN ?";SL
60  XS(1) = 0.0:XS(2) = SL
70  PRINT : INPUT "LENGTH OF RH SPAN ?";SR
80  XS(3) = SL + SR
90  PRINT : INPUT "DISTANCE OF HINGE FROM LH SUPPORT ?";SH
92  HOME : PRINT : PRINT "DATA SUMMARY": PRINT : PRINT
94  PRINT "LENGTH OF LH SPAN = ";SL;L$: PRINT : PRINT "LENGTH OF RH SPAN
    = ";SR;L$: PRINT
96  PRINT "DISTANCE OF HINGE FROM LH SUPPORT = ";SH;L$: PRINT
98  PRINT : INPUT "ANY CHANGES ?";A$: IF A$ = "Y" THEN 50
100  PRINT : PRINT "ILD REQUIRED FOR BM,SF OF REACTION B/S/R ": INPUT I$
105  IF I$ = "R" THEN 550
110  PRINT : INPUT "DISTANCE OF SECTION FROM LH SUPPORT ?";XB
120  IF I$ = "S" THEN 360
130  IF SH > XS(2) THEN 260
140  IF XB < XS(2) THEN 190
145  V(1) = 0.0:V(3) = 0.0:V(5) = 0.0:X(1) = 0.0:X(2) = SH:X(3) = XS(2):X(
     4) = XB:X(5) = XS(3)
147  IF XB = XS(2) THEN X(4) = - 1
148  IF XB = XS(3) THEN X(4) = - 1
150  V(4) = - (XS(3) - XB) * (XB - XS(2)) / (XS(3) - XS(2))
160  V(2) = (XS(3) - XB) * (XS(2) - SH) / (XS(3) - XS(2))
170  GOTO 340
190  IF XB < SH THEN 230
200  V(1) = 0.0:V(3) = 0.0:V(4) = 0.0:V(5) = 0.0:X(1) = 0.0:X(2) = SH:X(3)
     = XB:X(4) = XS(2):X(5) = XS(3)
205  IF XB = SH THEN X(3) = - 1
206  IF XB = XS(2) THEN X(3) = - 1
210  V(2) = XB - SH
220  GOTO 340
230  V(1) = 0.0:V(2) = 0.0:V(3) = 0.0:V(5) = 0.0:X(1) = 0.0:X(2) = XB:X(3)
     = SH:X(4) = XS(2):X(5) = XS(3)
235  IF XB = 0.0 THEN X(2) = - 1
236  IF XB = SH THEN X(2) = - 1
240  V(2) = - (SH - XB) * XB / SH
250  GOTO 340
260  IF XB < SH THEN 290
270  V(1) = 0.0:V(2) = 0.0:V(3) = 0.0:V(5) = 0.0:X(1) = 0.0:X(2) = XS(2):X
     (3) = SH:X(4) = XB:X(5) = XS(3)
275  IF XB = XS(3) THEN X(4) = - 1
```

```
276  IF XB = SH THEN X(4) = - 1
280  V(4) = - (XB - SH) * (XS(3) - XB) / (XS(3) - SH): GOTO 340
290  IF XB < XS(2) THEN 320
300  V(1) = 0.0:V(3) = 0.0:V(5) = 0.0:X(1) = 0.0:X(2) = XS(2):X(3) = XB:X(
     4) = SH:X(5) = XS(3)
305  IF XB = SH THEN X(3) = - 1
306  IF XB = XS(2) THEN X(3) = - 1
310  V(4) = SH - XB: GOTO 340
320  V(1) = 0.0:V(3) = 0.0:V(5) = 0.0:X(1) = 0.0:X(2) = XB:X(3) = XS(2):X(
     4) = SH:X(5) = XS(3)
326  IF XB = 0.0 THEN X(2) = - 1
327  IF XB = XS(2) THEN X(2) = - 1
330  V(2) = - XB * (XS(2) - XB) / (XS(2) - XS(1)):V(4) = XB * (SH - XS(2)
     ) / (XS(2) - XS(1))
340  PRINT : PRINT : PRINT "PEAK VALUES FOR ILD FOR BENDING MOMENT"
350  PRINT : PRINT "AT SECTION ";XB;L$;" FROM LH SUPPORT": PRINT :NV = 5:
     GOTO 750
360  IF SH > XS(2) THEN 450
370  IF XB < = XS(2) THEN 400
380  V(1) = 0.0:V(3) = 0.0:V(6) = 0.0:X(1) = 0.0:X(2) = SH:X(3) = XS(2):X(
     4) = XB:X(5) = XB:X(6) = XS(3)
385  IF XB = XS(3) THEN X(6) = - 1
390  V(2) = - (XS(2) - SH) / (XS(3) - XS(2)):V(4) = (XB - XS(2)) / (XS(3)
     - XS(2))
395  V(5) = V(4) - 1: GOTO 530
400  IF XB < SH THEN 430
410  V(1) = 0.0:V(5) = 0.0:V(6) = 0.0:X(1) = 0.0:X(2) = SH:X(3) = XB:X(4) =
     XB:X(5) = XS(2):X(6) = XS(3)
415  IF XB = SH THEN X(2) = - 1
416  IF XB = XS(2) THEN X(5) = - 1
420  V(2) = 1.0:V(3) = 1.0:V(4) = 0.0: GOTO 530
430  V(1) = 0.0:V(4) = 0.0:V(5) = 0.0:V(6) = 0.0:X(1) = 0.0:X(2) = XB:X(3)
     = XB:X(4) = SH:X(5) = XS(2):X(6) = XS(3)
435  IF XB = 0.0 THEN X(1) = - 1
440  V(2) = XB / SH:V(3) = V(2) - 1.0: GOTO 530
450  IF XB < SH THEN 480
460  V(1) = 0.0:V(2) = 0.0:V(3) = 0.0:V(6) = 0.0:X(1) = 0.0:X(2) = XS(2):X
     (3) = SH:X(4) = XB:X(5) = XB:X(6) = XS(3)
465  IF XB = XS(3) THEN X(6) = - 1
466  IF XB = SH THEN X(3) = - 1
470  V(4) = 1 - (XS(3) - XB) / (XS(3) - SH):V(5) = V(4) - 1: GOTO 530
480  IF XB < XS(2) THEN 510
490  V(1) = 0.0:V(2) = 0.0:V(6) = 0.0:X(1) = 0.0:X(2) = XS(2):X(3) = XB:X(
     4) = XB:X(5) = SH:X(6) = XS(3)
```

```
495  IF XB = XS(2) THEN X(3) = - 1
500  V(3) = 0.0:V(4) = - 1:V(5) = - 1: GOTO 530
510  V(1) = 0.0:V(4) = 0.0:V(6) = 0.0:X(1) = 0.0:X(2) = XS(2):X(3) = XB:X(
     4) = XB:X(5) = SH:X(6) = XS(3)
515  IF XB = 0.0 THEN X(1) = - 1
520  V(2) = XB / (XS(2) - XS(1)):V(3) = V(2) - 1:V(5) = (SH - XS(2)) / XS(
     2)
530  PRINT : PRINT : PRINT "PEAK VALUES FOR ILD FOR SHEAR FORCE"
540  PRINT : PRINT "AT SECTION ";XB;L$;" FROM LH SUPPORT": PRINT :NV = 6:
     GOTO 740
550  PRINT : PRINT "ILD FOR WHICH SUPPORT REACTION ?"
560  PRINT : PRINT "TYPE 1 FOR LEFT HAND SUPPORT"
570  PRINT : PRINT "TYPE 2 FOR CENTRAL SUPPORT"
580  PRINT : PRINT "TYPE 3 FOR RIGHT HAND SUPPORT"
590  PRINT : INPUT S
595  R$(1) = "LEFT HAND":R$(2) = "CENTRAL":R$(3) = "RIGHT HAND"
600  IF SH > XS(2) THEN 670
610  X(1) = 0.0:X(2) = SH:X(3) = XS(2):X(4) = XS(3)
620  IF S > 1 THEN 635
630  V(1) = 1:V(2) = 0.0:V(3) = 0.0:V(4) = 0.0: GOTO 730
635  IF S > 2 THEN 660
640  V(1) = 0.0:V(2) = (XS(3) - SH) / (XS(3) - XS(2)):V(3) = 1:V(4) = 0.0:
     GOTO 730
660  V(1) = 0.0:V(2) = - (XS(2) - SH) / (XS(3) - XS(2)):V(3) = 0.0:V(4) =
     1: GOTO 730
670  X(1) = 0.0:X(2) = XS(2):X(3) = SH:X(4) = XS(3)
680  IF S > 1 THEN 700
690  V(1) = 1.0:V(2) = 0.0:V(3) = - (SH - XS(2)) / (XS(2) - XS(1))
695  V(4) = 0.0: GOTO 730
700  IF S > 2 THEN 720
710  V(1) = 0.0:V(2) = 1.0:V(3) = (SH - XS(1)) / (XS(2) - XS(1)):V(4) = 0.
     0: GOTO 730
720  V(1) = 0.0:V(2) = 0.0:V(3) = 0.0:V(4) = 1.0
730  PRINT : PRINT : PRINT "PEAK VALUES FOR ILD FOR ";R$(S);" REACTION":N
     V = 4
740  PRINT : PRINT TAB( 3);"DISTANCE"; TAB( 20);"VALUE"
750  FOR I = 1 TO NV
753  IF X(I) = - 1 THEN 800
755  IF X(I + 1) = X(I) THEN 770
760  PRINT TAB( 3);X(I); TAB( 20);V(I): PRINT : GOTO 800
770  PRINT TAB( 3);X(I);"-"; TAB( 20);V(I): PRINT
780  PRINT TAB( 3);X(I + 1);"+"; TAB( 20);V(I + 1): PRINT
790  I = I + 1
800  NEXT I
```

```
810   PRINT : INPUT "ANY OTHER ILDS REQUIRED ?";A$
815   FOR I = 1 TO 7:X(I) = 0: NEXT I
820   IF A$ = "Y" THEN 100
830   END
```

Program notes

(1) Much of the program is involved in the evaluation of the peak, principal values for the ILDs for bending moment (lines 130–340), shear force (Lines 360–530) and reactions (lines 610–730). Using Virtual Work to establish the shapes of the diagrams (which are similar to those shown in Figure 7.2), general expressions for peak values can be found. These depend on whether the hinge is in the left-hand or right-hand span and the position of the section. Up to five or six different combinations of positions of section and hinge are considered which accounts for the length of the program.

(2) Lines 5–110   Input of data, summary and change option.

(3) Lines 110–350   Calculation of peak values for the ILD for bending moment. These are printed out from 750 onwards.

(4) Lines 360–540   Calculation of peak values for the ILD for shear force. These are printed out from 750 onwards.

(5) Lines 550–800   Peak ILD values for any of the three reactions are calculated and printed out.

The run shown below is for a two-span beam with span 10 m (left hand) and 5 m (right hand). The hinge is in the centre of the left-hand span and ILDs are to be drawn for the bending moment and shear force at a section 1 m to the right of the central support as well as the reaction in this support.

```
DATA FOR ILDS FOR TWO SPAN

HINGED BEAMS - PEAK VALUES ONLY

LENGTH UNITS ?M

LENGTH OF LH SPAN ?10

LENGTH OF RH SPAN ?5

DISTANCE OF HINGE FROM LH SUPPORT ?5

DATA SUMMARY


LENGTH OF LH SPAN = 10M

LENGTH OF RH SPAN = 5M

DISTANCE OF HINGE FROM LH SUPPORT = 5M
```

```
ANY CHANGES ?N

ILD REQUIRED FOR BM,SF OF REACTION B/S/R
?B

DISTANCE OF SECTION FROM LH SUPPORT ?11


PEAK VALUES FOR ILD FOR BENDING MOMENT

AT SECTION 11M FROM LH SUPPORT


    DISTANCE          VALUE
    0                 0

    5                 4

    10                0

    11                -.8

    15                0


ANY OTHER ILDS REQUIRED ?Y

ILD REQUIRED FOR BM,SF OF REACTION B/S/R
?R

ILD FOR WHICH SUPPORT REACTION ?

TYPE 1 FOR LEFT HAND SUPPORT

TYPE 2 FOR CENTRAL SUPPORT

TYPE 3 FOR RIGHT HAND SUPPORT

?2


PEAK VALUES FOR ILD FOR CENTRAL REACTION
    DISTANCE          VALUE
    0                 0

    5                 2

    10                1

    15                0

    15                0


ANY OTHER ILDS REQUIRED ?N
```

Example 7.3 ILDs for truss member forces

In the Warren truss shown in Figure 7.3(a), all the internal angles are
60° and $AB = BC = CD = DE = 1$ m. Draw the ILDs for the force in

member GC and the vertical deflection of joint B. Take $EA = 10^5$ kN and the load path as ABCDE.

```
10   HOME : PRINT : PRINT "INFLUENCE LINE DIAGRAMS FOR TRUSS": PRINT
15   DIM X(20),Y(20),EP(20),EN(20),EA(20),P(20,20),CM(20,20),MF(20,20),ME(
     20,20),D(20,20)
16   DIM LE(20),JE(20)
18   R$(1) = "FIRST":R$(2) = "SECOND":R$(3) = "THIRD":R$(4) = "FOURTH":R$(5
     ) = "FIFTH":R$(6) = "SIXTH":R$(7) = "SEVENTH":R$(8) = "EIGHTH"
20   INPUT "NUMBER OF MEMBERS IN TRUSS ?";NM: PRINT
30   INPUT "NUMBER OF JOINTS (INCLUDING SUPPORTS) ?";NJ: PRINT
32   INPUT "UNITS OF LENGTH M OR MM ?";L$: PRINT
34   INPUT "UNITS OF DISPLACEMENT M OR MM ?";W$: PRINT
40   FOR I = 1 TO NJ
42   PRINT "X-COORD OF JOINT ";I: INPUT X(I): PRINT
44   PRINT "Y-COORD OF JOINT ";I: INPUT Y(I): PRINT
46   NEXT I
50   FOR I = 1 TO NM: PRINT "POSITIVE END JOINT NO FOR MEMBER";I: INPUT EP
     (I)
60   PRINT : PRINT "NEGATIVE END JOINT NO FOR MEMBER ";I: INPUT EN(I)
70   PRINT : PRINT "CONSISTENT EA VALUE FOR MEMBER ";I: INPUT EA(I): PRINT

75   NEXT I
80   HOME : PRINT : PRINT "DATA SUMMARY": PRINT : PRINT
90   PRINT "NUMBER OF MEMBERS = ";NM: PRINT
100  PRINT "NUMBER OF JOINTS = ";NJ: PRINT
110  PRINT  TAB( 3);"JOINT NO"; TAB( 15);"X-COORD"; TAB( 27);"Y-COORD": PRINT

120  FOR I = 1 TO NJ: PRINT  TAB( 3);I; TAB( 15);X(I); TAB( 27);Y(I): NEXT
     I
125  PRINT : INPUT "PRESS RETURN TO CONTINUE";A$: HOME
130  PRINT : PRINT  TAB( 3);"MEMBER"; TAB( 13);"+VE END"; TAB( 23);"-VE E
     ND"; TAB( 33);"EA": PRINT
140  FOR I = 1 TO NM: PRINT  TAB( 3);I; TAB( 13);EP(I); TAB( 23);EN(I); TAB(
     33);EA(I): NEXT I
150  INPUT " DO YOU WISH TO CHANGE ANYTHING ?";A$
160  IF A$ = "Y" THEN 20
170  FOR I = 1 TO NM: FOR J = 1 TO NM:P(I,J) = 0.0: IF I = J THEN P(I,J) =
     - 1.0
175  NEXT J: NEXT I
180  PRINT : PRINT "BUILD UP TENSION COEFF EQNS JOINT BY JOINT": PRINT
185  R = 0:R1 = 0
190  PRINT : PRINT : INPUT "JOINT NO ?";I:FI = 0:R = R + 1:JE(I) = R: IF
     2 * R - 1 - R1 > NM THEN 320
```

```
200  PRINT : INPUT "IS JOINT RESTRAINED Y/N ?";A$: IF A$ = "N" THEN 220
210  INPUT "IN X-DIRN (1) OR Y-DIRN (2) ?";FI
220  PRINT : PRINT "NO OF MEMBERS MEETING AT JOINT ";I: INPUT NO
230  FOR II = 1 TO NO: PRINT "GIVE NO OF THE ";R$(II);" MEMBER ": PRINT "
     MEETING AT JOINT": INPUT J
240  K = EP(J):L = EN(J):HP = X(K) - X(L): IF I = K THEN HP = - HP
250  VP = Y(K) - Y(L): IF I = K THEN VP = - VP
255  LE(J) = SQR (HP * HP + VP * VP)
260  IF FI > 0 THEN 275
265  CM(2 * R - 1 - R1,J) = HP: IF 2 * R - 1 - R1 = NM THEN 290
270  CM(2 * R - R1,J) = VP: GOTO 290
275  V = HP: IF FI = 1 THEN V = VP
280  CM(2 * R - 1 - R1,J) = V
290  NEXT II
295  IF FI > 0 THEN R1 = R1 + 1
300  PRINT : INPUT "ANY MORE JOINTS ?";A$
310  IF A$ = "Y" THEN 190
320  PRINT : PRINT "NO MORE JOINTS REQUIRED,SUFFICIENT"
330  PRINT "EQUATIONS,PROCEEDING TO SOLUTION"
340  N = NM: GOSUB 3000
345  PRINT : PRINT "DO NOT DISTURB !!": PRINT : PRINT "FORCES AND DISPS B
     EING CALCULATED": PRINT : PRINT
350  FOR I = 1 TO NM: FOR J = 1 TO NM
360  MF(I,J) = P(I,J) * LE(I):ME(I,J) = MF(I,J) * LE(I) / EA(I)
370  NEXT J: NEXT I
380  FOR I = 1 TO NM: FOR J = 1 TO NM
390  D(I,J) = 0.0
400  FOR K = 1 TO NM:D(I,J) = D(I,J) + MF(K,I) * ME(K,J): NEXT K
410  NEXT J: NEXT I
420  PRINT : PRINT "FORCES AND DISPLACEMENTS DETERMINED !": PRINT
430  PRINT : INPUT "NUMBER OF 'FREE' JOINTS ON LOAD PATH ?";JF
440  FOR I = 1 TO JF: PRINT : PRINT "JOINT NO ";I;" ON LOAD PATH": INPUT
     LP(I): NEXT I
450  PRINT : PRINT "ILD REQUIRED FOR MEMBER FORCE"
455  PRINT "OR JOINT DISPLACEMENT  F/D": INPUT I$
460  IF I$ = "D" THEN 540
470  PRINT : INPUT "MEMBER FOR WHICH FORCE ILD REQUIRED ?";MN
480  FOR I = 1 TO JF:J = LP(I):J = JE(J):V(I) = MF(MN,2 * J): NEXT I
490  PRINT : PRINT "ILD VALUES FOR FORCE IN MEMBER ";MN
500  PRINT : PRINT : PRINT "JOINT NUMBER"; TAB( 20);"VALUE"
510  FOR I = 1 TO JF: PRINT : PRINT  TAB( 3);LP(I); TAB( 20);V(I): NEXT I
530  GOTO 640
540  PRINT : INPUT "JOINT FOR WHICH DISPLACEMENT ILD REQUIRED ?";MJ
550  PRINT : INPUT "VERTICAL OR HORIZONTAL COMPONENT V/H ?";D$
```

```
555 J = 2 * JE(MJ): IF D$ = "H" THEN J = J - 1
560 FOR I = 1 TO JF
580 K = LP(I):K = JE(K):V(I) = D(J,2 * K): NEXT I
590 O$ = "VERTICAL": IF D$ = "H" THEN O$ = "HORIZONTAL"
600 PRINT : PRINT "ILD VALUES FOR ";O$;" DISPLACEMENT"
610 PRINT : PRINT "COMPONENT AT JOINT ";MJ
620 PRINT : PRINT : PRINT "JOINT NUMBER"; TAB( 20);"VALUE";W$
630 FOR I = 1 TO JF: PRINT : PRINT TAB( 3);LP(I); TAB( 20);V(I): NEXT I

640 PRINT : INPUT "ANY OTHER ILDS REQUIRED Y/N ?";A$
650 IF A$ = "Y" THEN 450
660 END
3000 REM  MULTI RHS SOLVER
3010 MG = N - 1
3020 FOR IG = 1 TO MG: IF CM(IG,IG) < > 0.0 THEN 3090
3030 FOR NG = IG + 1 TO N:KG = NG: IF CM(NG,IG) < > 0.0 THEN 3070
3040 IF NG < N THEN 3060
3050 PRINT "SINGULAR MATRIX - NO SOLUTION POSSIBLE !"
3060 NEXT NG
3070 FOR PG = IG TO N:VV = CM(KG,PG):CM(KG,PG) = CM(IG,PG):CM(IG,PG) = V
     V: NEXT PG
3080 FOR PG = 1 TO N:VV = P(KG,PG):P(KG,PG) = P(IG,PG):P(IG,PG) = VV: NEXT
     PG
3090 LG = IG + 1
3095 PRINT : PRINT "PROCESSING EQUATION ";IG
3100 FOR JG = LG TO N: IF CM(JG,IG) = 0.0 THEN 3130
3110 FOR PG = LG TO N:CM(JG,PG) = CM(JG,PG) - CM(IG,PG) * CM(JG,IG) / CM
     (IG,IG): NEXT PG
3120 FOR PG = 1 TO N:P(JG,PG) = P(JG,PG) - P(IG,PG) * CM(JG,IG) / CM(IG,
     IG): NEXT PG
3130 NEXT JG: NEXT IG
3140 FOR PG = 1 TO N:P(N,PG) = P(N,PG) / CM(N,N): NEXT PG
3150 FOR IG = 1 TO MG:KG = N - IG
3155 PRINT : PRINT "BACKSUBSTITUTION,EQUATION ";KG
3160 FOR JG = KG + 1 TO N
3170 FOR PG = 1 TO N:P(KG,PG) = P(KG,PG) - P(JG,PG) * CM(KG,JG): NEXT PG

3175 NEXT JG
3180 FOR PG = 1 TO N:P(KG,PG) = P(KG,PG) / CM(KG,KG): NEXT PG
3190 NEXT IG
3200 RETURN
```

Program notes

(1) Lines 10–340 Essentially the same as the tension coefficient truss force analysis program given in Example 4.3. However, the load vector is replaced by P(NM,NM) which is a diagonal matrix with diagonal terms set to −1.0 (Line 170). This represents unit loads placed successively at each joint (note that you choose an arbitrary numbering of the joints – Line 190) in the positive x and y-directions (arbitrary).

(2) Lines 340–430 After solving for the NM sets of unit loads (Line 340), member forces and extensions (350–370) and joint displacements (380–410) due to each unit load are calculated. Virtual work methods are used to find the joint displacements; the extensions due to a unit load placed at a given joint and in a given direction are multiplied by the member forces due to unit loads applied to each joint and in each direction in succession. Thus the displacement matrix D (Line 400) has NM columns each giving the joint displacement components (in the order you specify) for a unit load applied horizontally then vertically at each joint (again in the order you specify as data for the program).

(3) Line 430 'Free' joints are those free to move in the direction of the unit load.

(4) Line 470–530 ILD values for the force in the chosen member (470) printed out at the positions of the joints on the loading path. These are the forces induced in the member by the unit load applied in the appropriate direction at each node.

(5) Lines 540–630 ILD values for the vertical or horizontal displacement at a joint, printed out at the positions of the joints on the loading path (Line 580).

(6) Lines 3000–3200 Gaussian elimination and backsubstitution subroutine for solving for NM load vectors (see Problem (5.4)).

A printout for the problem is given using the numbering scheme shown in Figure 7.4. Note that a reduced printout is given with much of the interactive data input of 10–330 excluded.

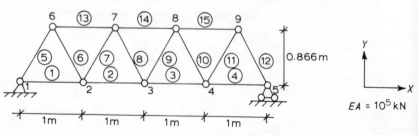

Figure 7.4

DATA SUMMARY

NUMBER OF MEMBERS = 15

NUMBER OF JOINTS = 9

JOINT NO	X-COORD	Y-COORD
1	0	0
2	1	0
3	2	0
4	3	0
5	4	0
6	.5	.866
7	1.5	.866
8	2.5	.866
9	3.5	.866

PRESS RETURN TO CONTINUE

MEMBER	+VE END	-VE END	EA
1	2	1	100000
2	3	2	100000
3	4	3	100000
4	5	4	100000
5	6	1	100000
6	6	2	100000
7	7	2	100000
8	7	3	100000
9	8	3	100000
10	8	4	100000
11	9	4	100000
12	9	5	100000
13	7	6	100000
14	8	7	100000
15	9	8	100000

DO YOU WISH TO CHANGE ANYTHING ?N

BUILD UP TENSION COEFF EQNS JOINT BY JOINT

JOINT NO ?2

IS JOINT RESTRAINED Y/N ?N

NO OF MEMBERS MEETING AT JOINT 2
?4
GIVE NO OF THE FIRST MEMBER
MEETING AT JOINT
?1
GIVE NO OF THE SECOND MEMBER
MEETING AT JOINT
?6
GIVE NO OF THE THIRD MEMBER
MEETING AT JOINT
?7
GIVE NO OF THE FOURTH MEMBER
MEETING AT JOINT
?2

ANY MORE JOINTS ?Y

```
JOINT NO ?3

IS JOINT RESTRAINED Y/N ?N

NO OF MEMBERS MEETING AT JOINT 3
?4
GIVE NO OF THE FIRST MEMBER
MEETING AT JOINT
?2
GIVE NO OF THE SECOND MEMBER
MEETING AT JOINT
?8
GIVE NO OF THE THIRD MEMBER
MEETING AT JOINT
?9
GIVE NO OF THE FOURTH MEMBER
MEETING AT JOINT
?3

ANY MORE JOINTS ?Y




JOINT NO ?4

IS JOINT RESTRAINED Y/N ?N

NO OF MEMBERS MEETING AT JOINT 4
?4
GIVE NO OF THE FIRST MEMBER
MEETING AT JOINT
?4
GIVE NO OF THE SECOND MEMBER
MEETING AT JOINT
?3
GIVE NO OF THE THIRD MEMBER
MEETING AT JOINT
?10
GIVE NO OF THE FOURTH MEMBER
MEETING AT JOINT
?11

ANY MORE JOINTS ?Y




JOINT NO ?5

IS JOINT RESTRAINED Y/N ?Y
IN X-DIRN (1) OR Y-DIRN (2) ?2

NO OF MEMBERS MEETING AT JOINT 5
?2
GIVE NO OF THE FIRST MEMBER
MEETING AT JOINT
?4
GIVE NO OF THE SECOND MEMBER
MEETING AT JOINT
?12

ANY MORE JOINTS ?Y




JOINT NO ?6

IS JOINT RESTRAINED Y/N ?N
```

```
NO OF MEMBERS MEETING AT JOINT 6
?3
GIVE NO OF THE FIRST MEMBER
MEETING AT JOINT
?5
GIVE NO OF THE SECOND MEMBER
MEETING AT JOINT
?6
GIVE NO OF THE THIRD MEMBER
MEETING AT JOINT
?13

ANY MORE JOINTS ?Y


JOINT NO ?7

IS JOINT RESTRAINED Y/N ?N

NO OF MEMBERS MEETING AT JOINT 7
?4
GIVE NO OF THE FIRST MEMBER
MEETING AT JOINT
?13
GIVE NO OF THE SECOND MEMBER.
MEETING AT JOINT
?7
GIVE NO OF THE THIRD MEMBER
MEETING AT JOINT
?8
GIVE NO OF THE FOURTH MEMBER
MEETING AT JOINT
?14

ANY MORE JOINTS ?Y


JOINT NO ?8

IS JOINT RESTRAINED Y/N ?N

NO OF MEMBERS MEETING AT JOINT 8
?4
GIVE NO OF THE FIRST MEMBER
MEETING AT JOINT
?14
GIVE NO OF THE SECOND MEMBER
MEETING AT JOINT
?9
GIVE NO OF THE THIRD MEMBER
MEETING AT JOINT
?10
GIVE NO OF THE FOURTH MEMBER
MEETING AT JOINT
?15

ANY MORE JOINTS ?Y


JOINT NO ?9

IS JOINT RESTRAINED Y/N ?N

NO OF MEMBERS MEETING AT JOINT 9
?3
GIVE NO OF THE FIRST MEMBER
MEETING AT JOINT
```

```
?15
GIVE NO OF THE SECOND MEMBER
MEETING AT JOINT
?11
GIVE NO OF THE THIRD MEMBER
MEETING AT JOINT
?12

ANY MORE JOINTS ?N

NO MORE JOINTS REQUIRED,SUFFICIENT
EQUATIONS,PROCEEDING TO SOLUTION

DO NOT DISTURB !!

FORCES AND DISPS BEING CALCULATED



FORCES AND DISPLACEMENTS DETERMINED !

NUMBER OF 'FREE' JOINTS ON LOAD PATH ?3


JOINT NO 1 ON LOAD PATH
?2

JOINT NO 2 ON LOAD PATH
?3

JOINT NO 3 ON LOAD PATH
?4

ILD REQUIRED FOR MEMBER FORCE
OR JOINT DISPLACEMENT  F/D
?F

MEMBER FOR WHICH FORCE ILD REQUIRED ?7

ILD VALUES FOR FORCE IN MEMBER 7
```

JOINT NUMBER	VALUE
2	-.288677252
3	.577354503
4	.288677251

```
ANY OTHER ILDS REQUIRED Y/N ?Y

ILD REQUIRED FOR MEMBER FORCE
OR JOINT DISPLACEMENT  F/D
?D

JOINT FOR WHICH DISPLACEMENT ILD REQUIRED ?2

VERTICAL OR HORIZONTAL COMPONENT V/H ?V

ILD VALUES FOR VERTICAL DISPLACEMENT

COMPONENT AT JOINT 2
```

```
JOINT NUMBER          VALUEMM

    2                 4.08344089E-05

    3                 3.83347023E-05

    4                 2.250088E-05

ANY OTHER ILDS REQUIRED Y/N ?Y

ILD REQUIRED FOR MEMBER FORCE
OR JOINT DISPLACEMENT   F/D
?F

MEMBER FOR WHICH FORCE ILD REQUIRED ?8

ILD VALUES FOR FORCE IN MEMBER 8


JOINT NUMBER          VALUE

    2                 .288677252

    3                 -.577354503

    4                 -.288677252

ANY OTHER ILDS REQUIRED Y/N ?N
```

Joint 5 is restrained in the y-direction and 2 should be returned after the request in Line 210.

Since y is positive upwards, unit loads are applied *upwards* at all joints. The ILD values given above reflect this. In the case of the member force in GC (member 8), tensile values are *positive* and when the (*upward*) unit load is applied at joint 2(B), a tensile force is induced in GC. It may thus be better to take the y-axis as positive downwards.

In the case of the vertical displacements for the deflection ILD, these are positive in the direction of the applied unit load.

PROBLEMS

(7.1) Use the three programs given in the worked examples to draw ILDs for various beams and trusses of your own choice. Check all results by using virtual work or other methods.

(7.2) If a simply supported beam overhangs either or both supports, use virtual work methods to find general expressions for the peak ILD values for the bending moment and shear force at points in the cantilever sections and between the supports. Change the program given in Example 7.1 to allow for overhanging beams.

(7.3) Taking a point distance x from the left-hand end of the overhanging beam of Problem (7.2), use Macaulay's method to find the deflection curve when a vertical unit load is applied. This is the ILD for vertical deflection at the chosen point. Change the program of Example 7.1 to print data for drawing this diagram.

(7.4) Use virtual work methods to find general expressions for the peak values of ILDs for the reactions at the supports of an overhanging simply supported beam. Incorporate these into the program you have developed for Problems (7.2) and (7.3).

(7.5) Show that a three-span beam with hinges in two spans is statically determinate. Use virtual work methods to determine general expressions for peak values of the bending moment and shear force ILDs at a point within the central span when the hinges are in the outer spans. How can the program of Example 7.2 be used to check your values? (Note that the three-span beam incorporates two two-span beams; (a) the central span and the right-hand span with a hinge and (b) the central span and the left-hand span with a hinge).

(7.6) For a three-span beam similar to that described in Problem (7.5), find and check peak values for the ILDs for all support reactions.

(7.7) Write a program that uses the peak ILD values from the programs supplied, together with Live Load and Dead Load specifications, as data for the evaluation of maximum and minimum shear force and bending moment at any chosen section. Consider the Live Loading to be a uniformly distributed load of length greater than the total length of the beam or truss (see Section (7.3).

You will need to locate points of zero value on the ILDs and possibly consider two or three positions of the Live Loading.

How would use use, or modify this program to

(a) Find the section giving the largest maximum or minimum values.
(b) Find the deflection at this or other sections (ILD data required)? Will the section with the largest bending moment have the largest deflection? If not how can this be found?

(7.8) With only moderate sized problems, the truss program of Example 7.3 requires a lot of data. Errors in the later stages of input, particularly when building up the equilibrium equations require *all* data to be re-input. There are two ways of avoiding this:

(a) Supply more frequent options to change data. These may be of the type shown in lines 150 and 160, but involving much smaller quantities of data.
(b) Store data on a disc file. On first running with new data, (a) above is used but data is stored on the disc as soon as it is satisfactory. On subsequent runs, input can be from the disc file.

Modify the program to offer both these options.

Appendix

A1.1 Mohr correction diagram

If the truss shown in Figure A1.1 is given a rigid body rotation about A through a small angle α, then, ignoring small horizontal movement, the vertical deflection components of C, E and G are, by proportion,

$$V_C = \frac{L}{4}\cdot\alpha = \frac{L}{4}\cdot\frac{\delta}{L} = \frac{\delta}{4}\uparrow;\ V_E = \frac{\delta}{2}\uparrow;\ V_G = \frac{3\delta}{4}\uparrow$$

Typically, at joint F, $V_F/S = \cos\theta = AG/AF$.

$S = \alpha.AF$, since every point will rotate through α about A.

Thus, $V_F = S.AG/AF = \alpha.AF.AG/AF = \alpha AG = \dfrac{3L}{4}\cdot\dfrac{\delta}{L} = \dfrac{3\delta}{4}\uparrow$,

$$V_D = \frac{\delta}{2}\uparrow \text{ and } V_B = \frac{\delta}{4}\uparrow$$

Also $H_F/S = \sin\theta = GF/AF$.
Thus $H_F = S.GF/AF = \alpha AF.GF/AF = \alpha.GF = h\delta/L\leftarrow$
and $H_D = H_B = H_F = h\delta/L\leftarrow$

In Figure A1.2 the fixed joint A becomes the point a' and the

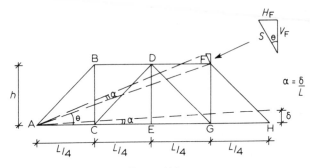

Figure A1.1

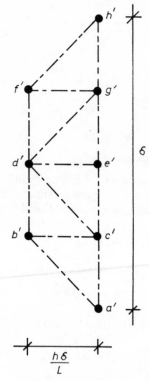

Figure A1.2

displacements of the joints calculated above are used to plot their new positions b', c', e', etc. relative to a'. Joining up these points (the dot–dash lines shown in Figure A1.2) shows that they are the joint locations of an equivalent scale diagram of the original structure rotated through 90° in the same direction as α (in this case anticlockwise). The scale is given by the magnitude of δ.

This quick method of constructing the displacement diagram for rigid body rotation (i.e. the Mohr correction diagram) is valid for any shape of structure providing the angle of rotation α is small and therefore, the horizontal displacement of joints such as C, E, G and H can be neglected.

Index

Butterworths BASIC Books

General Editors **M J Iremonger and P D Smith**

Like *BASIC Hydraulics*, these books not only introduce computer methods but also relate those methods to specific topics, so that students and practising engineers can benefit from the content of each book through the solution of real engineering and mathematical problems. Full information on all these titles is available from the publishers.

 Butterworths
Borough Green, Sevenoaks, Kent TN15 8PH